The Boys' First Book of

RADIO *and* ELECTRONICS

by ALFRED MORGAN

THE BOYS' FIRST BOOK OF

RADIO AND

ELECTRONICS

ILLUSTRATED BY THE AUTHOR AND WALT REED

CHARLES SCRIBNER'S SONS   NEW YORK

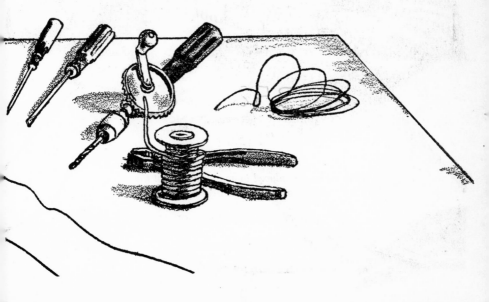

Library of Congress Catalog Card No. 54-8788

First Printing	October, 1954
Second Printing	November, 1955
Third Printing	April, 1956
Fourth Printing	April, 1957
Fifth Printing	April, 1958
Sixth Printing	May, 1959
Seventh Printing	May, 1960
Eighth Printing (Revised)	June, 1961
Ninth Printing	May, 1962

COPYRIGHT 1954 BY ALFRED MORGAN

I-5.62[H]

PRINTED IN THE UNITED STATES OF AMERICA

CONTENTS

The Boys' First Book of

RADIO *and* ELECTRONICS

Chapter One

THE FIRST WIRELESS TELEGRAPH and THE FIRST WIRELESS TELEPHONE

On March 3, 1899, the lightship *East Goodwin* was at anchor at her post off the coast of South Foreland, Great Britain. The beacon light at her masthead which sent its warning beam out into the night as a guide to passing ships was dimmed by a heavy fog which hung over the sea. The fog-horn aboard the *East Goodwin* was moaning its caution into the mist and rain at regular intervals. Between each warning wail there was only the sound of water slapping against the sides of the lightship. All else was ominously quiet. Both sound and vision were deadened by the vapor-laden air.

Suddenly there came a shout from the lightship and following it a shout from elsewhere in the fog. A black hull loomed out of the darkness and towered over the lightship. There was a crash and more shouting. The *East Goodwin* had been struck by a steamer off its course and the lightship was sinking. Help must come quickly to be in time. Then began a tiny snapping and crackling sound. It was hardly more than a faint sputtering but it was the *East Goodwin's* cry of distress—her appeal for help. This call from far out on the sea was heard ashore. Life boats put out to the rescue, and the members of the lightship's crew who would have been doomed to die in another age were soon brought safely back to land.

On that day, for the first time so far as is known, wireless telegraphy saved lives in a marine disaster. The faint sputtering sounds aboard the *East Goodwin* were made by Marconi's new wireless telegraph transmitter. The wireless telegraph had sent its call for help within a few minutes after the crash occurred and its message had brought the rescuers. Since then many ships, battered by the wind and waves, disabled and sinking or afire, have sent their calls for help out into space and aid has arrived in time. Thousands of people have been saved from a watery grave by the voice which wireless telegraphy gave to ships at sea.

The first wireless telegraph equipment aboard an Atlantic liner was installed (in 1900) on the Norddeutscher-Lloyd Steamship Company's *Kaiser Wilhelm der Grosse*. A year previously (1899) naval vessels were first provided with the wireless telegraph when the Marconi system was installed on three British battleships which were then dispatched to the scene of the Boer War and to the Sandwich Islands. Until 1899, when a vessel left port nothing was heard from her until she reached her destination, unless she was sighted by other passing ships and reported by them when they reached port. There was no way of communicating between the shore and a vessel out of sight of land. But after wireless telegraphy was invented, messages could be sent through space for hundreds of miles. Now all vessels of any size carry "radio." In America the term "radio" has replaced the old term "wireless." All passenger vessels are required by law to carry radio equipment. Many ships are provided with radio telephones which make it possible for any of the passengers and crew members aboard to be connected with any of the millions of telephones belonging to the Bell Telephone system even though the ship is in the middle of an ocean.

Radio broadcasting, telephony across oceans, television, radar and a multitude of other electronic marvels had their beginnings in the crude apparatus of the first wireless telegraph.

The whole history of their development would fill several large volumes. But it is an interesting story even when told very briefly. For a beginning, we first look in upon a city in Germany.

THE DISCOVERY OF ELECTRIC WAVES— HEINRICH RUDOLPH HERTZ

The German Empire was not ten years old when there was born in the city of Hamburg, Germany, a lusty red-faced baby. He was named Heinrich Rudolph Hertz.* Young Hertz grew to early manhood unnoticed and not in any way exceptional. Like many boys he had ambition to be a civil engineer, so at the age of twenty he went to a school in Munich to study for an engineering career. But in a short time all intentions to become an engineer left him. He wanted to study mathematics and physical science instead. He changed his plans and 1878 found young Hertz in Berlin enrolled as a student under two of the world's greatest scientists, von Helmholtz and Kirchhoff.

HEINRICH RUDOLPH HERTZ

This brilliant scientist was first to create and detect electromagnetic waves. His discoveries made possible wireless telegraphy. Efforts to improve the apparatus used for wireless telegraphy laid the foundation for electronics.

Seven years later he was appointed Professor of Physics at the Technical High School at Karlsruhe. Here in his Karlsruhe laboratory Hertz went to work on a scientific problem which had first come to his attention six years before while he was still a pupil. The problem he undertook was to demonstrate the theories of a Scotch physicist, James Clerk Maxwell. The mathematical calculations of this talented Scotsman iden-

* BORN: February 22, 1857, Hamburg, Germany. DIED: January 1, 1894, Bonn, Germany.

tified light with electrical energy. His calculations and theories showed that both are waves of some sort.

These ideas of Maxwell's were wonderful "on paper," but neither he nor any one else had been able to prove them by demonstrations. No one knew how to create electric waves. No one knew how to build or set up apparatus which would prove these theories.

Finally, one memorable day late in 1887, an announcement was made which thrilled every physical laboratory in the world. It occurred at a meeting of the Physical Society in Berlin. In an atmosphere of great expectancy, von Helmholtz, perhaps the most illustrious man in the German Empire next to Bismarck and the Emperor, solemnly announced that he would describe some remarkable experiments of a former pupil of his. He announced that *Hertz had produced electric waves* and told how it had been accomplished.

Hertz continued his experiments with electric waves and demonstrated that, though they are invisible, they resemble waves of light. He demonstrated that they possess many of the same properties as light; that they can be reflected from surfaces in accordance with the same laws as those of light waves. He found a way to measure electric waves and from their measurements he calculated their velocity and found it to be the same as light—186,000 miles a second.

Soon many scientists were experimenting with Hertz "oscillators" and "resonators," as the apparatus which Hertz had devised was called. The oscillator consisted of two metal plates, each fitted with a rod ending in a brass ball connected to an induction coil. When connected to a suitable battery, the induction coil produced high-voltage currents which charged the plates and then jumped across the space between the balls in the form of sparks. Each time a spark jumped between the balls it discharged the plates. Charging and discharging the plates rapidly in this manner produced electric waves which moved away from the oscillator and out into space.

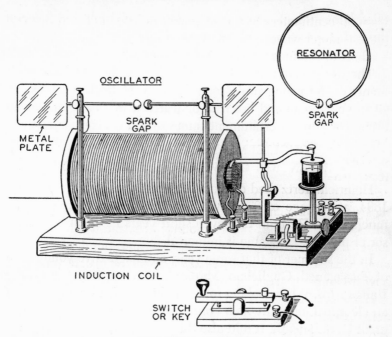

THE HERTZ APPARATUS
FOR CREATING AND DETECTING ELECTRIC WAVES

This is the apparatus that Hertz set up to prove Maxwell's theory that light and electrical energy are waves of some sort. Pressing the key or switch connected the induction coil to a battery and caused electric sparks to jump across the spark gap on the coil. Hertz called this part of his apparatus the oscillator. When sparks jumped across the oscillator spark gap, electric waves moved out into space and generated tiny sparks in the gap in a resonator near by. The Hertz resonator consisted of two metal balls attached to the end of a copper wire bent in a circle until the balls almost touched each other.

The resonator consisted of two brass balls fitted to the ends of a copper wire which was bent in a circle until the balls almost touched one another. When this ring was held near the oscillator and sparks from the induction coil leaped across the space between the balls connected to the metal plates the electric waves thus created caused tiny sparks to appear between the balls on the ring. By such means Hertz produced waves from 30 centimeters to a few meters in length. Today we call 30 centimeter waves ultra-short waves and use a more efficient method to produce them.

The wonders of radio are a direct consequence of the experiments of the young professor of physics at Karlsruhe. As you sit in your home and listen to or watch a football game or an orchestra, your entertainment comes to you via Hertzian waves.

GUGLIELMO MARCONI AND THE
INVENTION OF WIRELESS TELEGRAPHY

Heinrich Hertz died of blood poisoning on New Year's Day, 1894, at the age of 37. Few scientists have accomplished so much as did Hertz in the seven short years he spent as professor of physics. His name is immortal.

In the summer of that same year, an imaginative young man of 20, named Guglielmo Marconi, was vacationing in the Italian Alps. While looking for something to read, he picked up an electrical journal which contained an announcement of the great Hertz's death. It told also the story of Hertz's experiments with electric waves. Young Marconi read the story with great interest and an idea dawned in his mind.* Why couldn't telegraph signals be transmitted through the air without wires with the Hertz apparatus? Enthusiastic over this idea, he cut short his vacation and returned to his home near Bologna to try some experiments.

Marconi was not the first to have this idea. To put the idea into practical form was not easy. There was no quick answer at hand. It was not possible to build wireless telegraph instruments as soon as Hertz showed the world how to produce and detect electric waves. Otherwise some one would have produced a practical system of wireless telegraphy before Marconi.

* Marconi gained his initial knowledge of Hertz waves in much the same way that amateur wireless experimenters acquired the same knowledge in later years. HE READ ABOUT THEM. After he had become famous, Marconi related during an interview that in 1894 or 1895 he read an illustrated article in *Wiedemann's Annalen* dealing with Hertz's announcements and that he also read a book called *Inventions and Researches of Nikola Tesla* by T. C. Martin, published in 1894.

WILLIAM MARCONI—21 *year old inventor*—
AND HIS APPARATUS FOR SIGNALLING WITHOUT WIRES

July 17, 1897 the *Scientific American Supplement* (No. 1124) printed a discourse entitled "Signalling Through Space Without Wires" delivered before the Royal Institution June 4, 1897 by Sir William Preece. Over 50 years ago the author of this book clipped the article out and pasted it in his scrap book. The article was illustrated by engravings originally published in *L'Illustration and London Engineer*. The illustration above was sketched from one of these engravings by permission of the SCIENTIFIC AMERICAN. It apparently shows the wireless telegraph apparatus which Marconi took to England with him. This apparatus could do little more than prove that wireless telegraphy was possible. The Righi oscillator is at Marconi's left. Sir William Preece described the Righi oscillator as "two spheres of solid brass, 4 in. in diameter—fixed in an oil-tight case of insulating material, so that a hemisphere of each is exposed, the other hemisphere being immersed in a bath of vaseline oil." The Righi oscillator gave better results than the simpler Hertz Oscillator. The receiver is at Marconi's right. A telegraph sounder is mounted on top of the cabinet.

A Hertz resonator would not detect waves more than a few feet distant from the wave-producing Hertz oscillator. A practical wireless telegraph could not be made without first learning how to produce stronger electric waves than those Hertz had produced. A sensitive instrument to replace the Hertz resonator—

an instrument which would detect the electric waves at a great distance from the transmitter—a distance which could be measured in miles—was necessary.

An important step toward solving one of these problems had been made by the time young Marconi became interested.

Edouard Branly of Paris had made the first step when he demonstrated that electric waves would affect powdered metals. An electric current does not flow easily through a loosely packed powdered metal. Loose metal powder offers great resistance to the current. Branly showed that an electric current would pass through metal powder more easily after the powder had been struck by an electric wave. The wave caused the particles of powder to cling together or *cohere* and lowered their resistance to an electric current.

Branly also found that a mechanical shock, such as tapping the tube in which the powder was contained, caused the conductivity of the powder to disappear and restored its resistance to electric current. This knowledge enabled him to devise the "coherer" which he exhibited before the French Academy in 1891, thereby winning membership in that body.

Branly's coherer consisted of a glass tube filled with loose iron filings connected to a galvanometer and battery. A galvanometer is an instrument for measuring small electric currents. Electric waves produced by a Hertz oscillator 25 yards distant caused the iron filings to cohere (thus the name coherer) and the galvanometer to indicate an increase in the current flowing through the filings. A tapper arrangement, a tiny hammer like that on an electric bell, tapped the tube and shook the filings so that they were restored to a loose state.

We are accustomed to read and hear of poor boys who by hard work and ability became famous and often became rich. The life story of Guglielmo Marconi is not the usual rags-to-riches tale. He came from a family with adequate means. He had culture, education and some money but not a fortune. His father, Giuseppe Marconi, was an Italian banker. His mother

(nee Ann Jameson) was the youngest daughter of Andrew
Jameson of the well-known whiskey distillers of Dublin.
Guglielmo (the Italian for William) was the second son; he
had an older brother named Alfonso.

The idea that Hertzian waves might make it possible to
transmit telegraphic signals over distances great enough to be
of commercial value fascinated Guglielmo Marconi. He started
his experiments at his father's country home, the Villa Griffone,
at Pontecchio near Bologna. He brought together an induction coil, telegraph key, batteries, Branly coherer and Hertz
resonator.

The first tests were carried out with an ordinary Hertz oscillator and a Branly coherer as detector. The Branly coherer
was soon found to be far too erratic and unreliable for practical
work and was discarded. After many experiments, a coherer
having the same principle as Branly's but of Marconi's own
improved design proved to be remarkably sensitive and reliable.
It consisted of nickel and silver filings placed in a small gap
between two silver plugs in a glass tube. This improved coherer
made it possible to send wireless telegraph messages through
space for distances of almost a mile. A telegraph key placed in
the battery circuit at the transmitter made it possible to transmit waves for long or short periods corresponding to the dots
and dashes of the telegraph code.

In August, 1895, Marconi discovered that he could greatly
increase the distance between his transmitter and receiver by
connecting an elevated wire or antenna and the earth to both
the transmitting and the receiving apparatus. The coherer was
placed in a circuit containing a sensitive relay which operated
a "tapper" to shake the coherer and also operated a recording
instrument. This arrangement recorded on a paper tape the
telegraph signals made by pressing the key at the distant
transmitter.

In July, 1896, Marconi took a step which had an immense
influence on his future. He discontinued his experiments in

Italy and went to England. He was not yet twenty-two years old. He had no difficulty in obtaining a letter of introduction to Sir William Preece, then technical director of the British Post Office and one of the leading telegraph engineers of the day. The young scientist succeeded in convincing Preece that his ideas for a system of wireless telegraphy were practical and a number of experiments were made at Salisbury Plain and elsewhere in England.

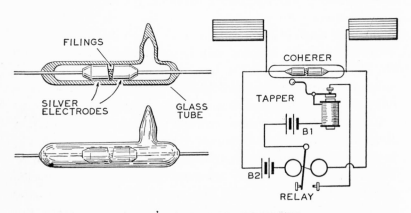

MARCONI'S COHERER AND ITS CIRCUIT

Marconi's improved form of Branly's coherer was the first practical detector. In a small glass tube about 4 centimeters long (about 1½ inches) and an internal diameter of 5 millimeters were placed two silver electrodes or plugs which fitted the tube tightly. To the plugs were attached platinum wires sealed through the closed ends of the tubes. The inner ends of the plugs were polished and about 2 millimeters apart. The space between the plugs was filled with nickel and silver filings (95 per cent nickel filings and 5 per cent silver filings). All the air was then pumped out of the tube and it was sealed.

The lower left hand sketch shows a Marconi coherer. Above it the same coherer is shown in section. The right hand sketch shows the circuit of the receiver. When radio waves passed through the coherer, the filings cohered and current from a battery (B2) flowed through the sensitive relay. The relay closed the tapper circuit and current from a battery (B1) operated the tapper and shook the filings apart so that they were ready for the next signal.

The first inkling that science might soon bestow such a marvel as a practical system of signalling through space for long distances without wires came to the world in general in June, 1897. On Friday evening, June 4, 1897, Sir William Preece told a meeting of the Royal Institution about young Marconi's successful experiments. Today when radio encircles the globe, when a "ham" in midwest U. S. A. can go into his "shack" and talk to another "ham" in Australia, it is interesting to read what Sir William had to say about the infant wireless at a time before its christening, when lacking a name, it was called "signalling through space without wires."

Here are some of Preece's words:

"The distance to which signals have been sent is remarkable. On Salisbury Plain, Mr. Marconi covered a distance of four miles. In Bristol Channel this has been extended to over eight miles and *we have by no means reached the limit.*"

In 1898, Marconi's new wireless telegraph was installed aboard the royal yacht Osborne. This enabled Queen Victoria to maintain constant communication with the then Prince of Wales (King Edward VII) who was convalescing from an illness aboard the yacht. The first commercial use of wireless occurred in this same year when Marconi sent a report of the Kingston Yacht Races to the *Dublin Express* from aboard the tug *Flying Huntress* in the Irish Sea. Wireless communication was established across the English Channel between France and England for the first time in March, 1899.

The now 24-year-old Marconi proved to be a young man of great courage and imagination. In his mind he foresaw telegrams flashing over the broad expanse of the Atlantic Ocean. He determined to make this vision a reality. A high-power transmitting station was built at Poldhu on the coast of Cornwall, England. Everything was on a much larger scale than Marconi had attempted previously. Professor J. A. Fleming was entrusted with designing and arranging the apparatus for generating the powerful alternating current which was to be employed at the transmitter. In addition to the work of Professor Fleming, valuable technical assistance was given by R. N. Vyvyan and W. S. Entwhistle.

GUGLIELMO MARCONI

Born April 23, 1874; died July 20, 1937. Marconi was the first to devise a practical system of wireless telegraphy. He did much experimenting with short waves and in 1922 suggested radar. Always modest, he said of his accomplishments that he had simply observed certain facts and developed instruments to meet them.

In December, 1901, Marconi went to Newfoundland. He took with him various receiving instruments and several balloons and kites for raising a 400-foot wire as a receiving antenna. He installed his apparatus in a building at Signal Hill, St. John's. A new wave detector replaced the Marconi coherer. The new detector was a simple device invented by Lieutenant Solari of the Italian Navy. It consisted of a tiny globule of mercury between two iron electrodes in a glass tube, connected to a battery and a telephone receiver. It was far more sensitive than the Marconi coherer.

The most thrilling moment of the young scientist's life came shortly after noon on December 12, 1901. Marconi and his two assistants listened in the telephone receiver and heard the feeble sounds, *dit dit dit*, repeated several times. This signal they knew had been flashed from the transmitting station set up on the southwest tip of England. It seemed almost too good to be true. Marconi listened again the following day and again the invisible waves came winging across the ocean to strike the slender copper wire held aloft by a kite and be led down to the instruments installed in the old barrack on Signal Hill, St. John's. Again a series of three sig-

FIRST TRANSATLANTIC RECEIVING STATION

Barracks at Signal Hill, St. John's, Newfoundland, where Marconi apparatus was set up for receiving the first transatlantic wireless signals Dec. 12, 1901. The receiving antenna was a slender wire held aloft by a kite.

nificant sounds corresponding to the letter S in the telegraph alphabet confirmed the fact that the trackless Atlantic had been spanned by Hertz's waves and Marconi's own ingenuity and daring. His dream had been realized.

Little did this quiet, modest, young inventor—or any one at

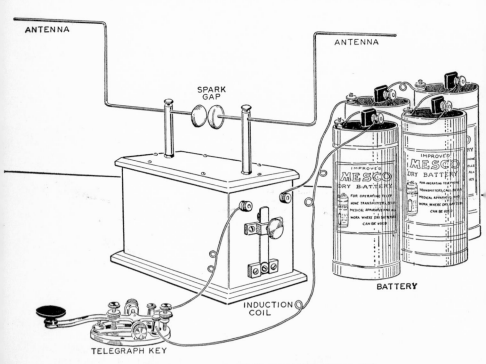

AN AMATEUR TRANSMITTER OF FIFTY YEARS AGO

Newspaper accounts about Marconi's experiments in England stimulated amateur scientists to build wireless telegraph instruments. In America just after the turn of the century, boys began to tinker with wireless telegraphy. Many of them were cultivating a hobby which later became their vocation. The first amateur transmitters and receivers were somewhat similar to Marconi's early apparatus and were capable only of sending messages across a large auditorium or from one room to another in the same house. The amateur transmitter of those days consisted of a spark coil fitted with a spark gap and connected to a key and battery.

that time—think that the same Guglielmo Marconi would be sitting in a comfortable room in London thirty years later to a day and in a quiet, conversational tone speak words that would be heard by millions of persons all over the world. Yet on December 11, 1931, Marconi's own voice and words of tribute to him from fifteen nations encircled the earth via radio-

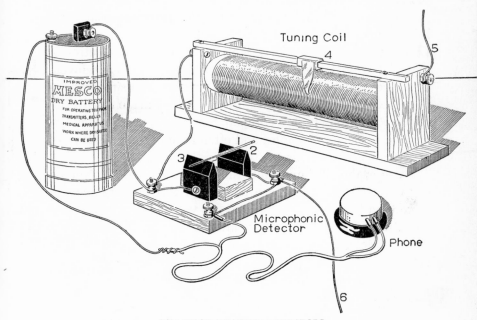

THE FIRST AMATEUR DETECTORS

The coherer of the early days of amateur wireless telegraphy was soon replaced by more sensitive "microphone" detectors. One form consisted of a steel sewing needle resting on the sharpened edges of two carbon blocks. The detector was connected to a dry cell and a telephone receiver. Microphonic detectors were soon superseded by electrolytic detectors and then by crystal detectors.

Amateur "coherer sets" were usually untuned. The first "detector sets" were tuned by a "single-slide tuner." The "slide" or slider was a movable contact on the tuning coil. Single-slide tuners were superseded by "double-slide" tuning coils. The latter gave way to "couplers" and the couplers to variometers. 1, needle, 2 and 3, carbon blocks; 4, slider; 5, antenna wire; 6, ground wire.

telephone in a world-wide celebration of the thirtieth anniversary of the first transatlantic wireless signals.

RADIO RESULTED
FROM THE WORK OF MANY MEN

Marconi was the pioneer who, by combining and improving the discoveries of Hertz, Branly and others, gave the first practical wireless telegraph to the world. But our present day radio is by no means the work of a single mind or even of a few minds. During the past six decades, thousands of radio and electronics patents have been granted to a long list of scientists and inventors. The pioneer wireless inventors worked with simple, comparatively crude tools. In most instances they made discoveries which others soon improved upon. Since then, radio inventions have become more complex and often require the assistance of experts in various fields.

There are many important "firsts" in radio and electronics, but unfortunately not space enough in this book to recount more than two or three of them. For young people who have an aptitude for science and are interested in reading about the first radiotelephone, the first vacuum tube, etc., and the men who invented them, there is a list of interesting books at the back of this volume. Some of these titles are available at the public libraries in many towns and cities.

REGINALD A. FESSENDEN
AND THE FIRST RADIO BROADCAST

It is probable that there are few people who could win the jackpot on a radio "quiz" program if the question happened to be, "Who was Reginald A. Fessenden? Can you tell me something he accomplished?"

Fessenden was an American radio pioneer and inventor. He was first to broadcast phonograph music and speech by means of Hertzian waves. He devised the first practical wireless telephone. U. S. Patent No. 706,747 for a practical wireless telephone was granted to him on August 12, 1902.

Fessenden was born and educated in Canada. His first job was that of principal of the Whitney Institute in Bermuda. But his interest in electricity was so great that he decided to give up teaching and go to New York in hopes of finding employment with Thomas A. Edison. He started as a tester with the Edison Machine Works and finally became one of Edison's assistants at the Llewellyn Park Laboratory. He acquired the title of Chief Chemist at the Laboratory. He left Edison's employ in 1889 to resume teaching again. Three years later he had become professor of electrical engineering at Purdue University. From there he went in turn to similar posts at the University of Pennsylvania and to Western University of Pennsylvania. At both of these institutions Fessenden lectured on Hertzian waves and carried out numerous experiments with them.

These facts about Fessenden's early career may be uninteresting to many readers of this book. They are recited here to show that youth need not be a handicap in scientific accomplishment. They add another name to the long list of very young men who achieved great things in science at an early age. Fessenden was 22 years of age when he was Edison's "Chief Chemist." It has been mentioned that Marconi was but 21 when he took his new wireless telegraph to England. Edwin H. Armstrong, about whom we will read more later, was a college student when he developed a radio circuit and a new principle in the use of electron tubes which were a revolutionary advance in radio. There is not space in this volume to cite the accomplishments of all the young men who contributed to the science of radio.

It is sometimes said that "everything has been discovered," and that young men today do not have much chance to do original things in science. This is not true. A good share of the new discoveries of the future will be made by scientific pioneers who have not long been old enough to vote.

Now, back to Fessenden. In December, 1899, a maker of scientific instruments in Washington, D. C., constructed a rotating commutator for Fessenden—probably from the joint designs of himself and Fessenden. The purpose of this device was to create an alternating current whose fluctuations would occur so rapidly as to be above the range of the human ear. It was planned to send this rapidly alternating current into an antenna and thereby produce Hertzian waves which would carry music and the human voice.

Fessenden did not test his invention until October, 1900. But with it, in December, 1900, Professor Fessenden transmitted SPEECH for the first time by Hertzian waves. In 1902 the National Electric Signalling Company was organized to develop Fessenden's ideas and inventions. His activities were then shifted to the Company's new station at Brant Rock, Massachusetts. On Christmas Eve, 1906, radio operators aboard ships

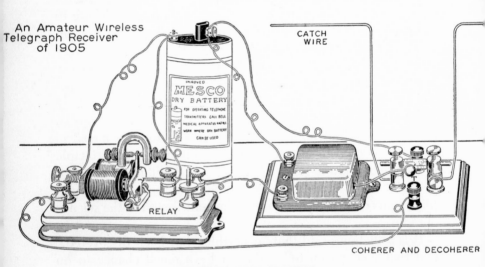

An Amateur Wireless Telegraph Receiver of 1905

CATCH WIRE

MESCO DRY BATTERY

RELAY

COHERER AND DECOHERER

EARLY AMATEUR RECEIVER

The amateur receiver of fifty years ago employed a simple version of Marconi's coherer. It consisted of a few nickel and silver filings between two metal plugs enclosed in a glass tube. The coherer was connected to a dry cell, a sensitive relay and to a tapper made from an old doorbell.

along the coast, long accustomed to hear only the dots and dashes of the telegraph code and the clicks and crashes of static in their headphones, were startled to hear voices and music. Ships reported reception as far down the coast as Virginia. This, the first broadcast, had been transmitted by the Brant Rock station. Later the voices were reported heard in New York, Washington, D. C., and New Orleans.

More than 500 inventions were attributed to Reginald Fessenden during the 30 years he was actively engaged in developing his imaginative ideas in the fields of Hertzian waves, sound and light. Marconi's feat of sending wireless telegraph signals across the Atlantic ocean remained unrivaled until 1906 when Fessenden equalled it. Those who became amateur radio operators or "hams" during the first decade of this century will remember the electrolytic detector and the rotary spark gap. They were both Fessenden inventions.

CHAPTER TWO

A FEW FACTS ABOUT ELECTRICITY

You may wish to skip this chapter and turn immediately to the pages which explain how to build radio receivers. Skip it if you wish—it is better not to do so. Here is the reason:

No doubt you will agree that in order to read or spell it is necessary to know the letters of the alphabet. It is equally true that you must know the "ABC's" of electricity before you can intelligently build radio and electronic apparatus. There are many electrical processes involved in radio and electronics. The ABC's of electricity are a few fundamental facts or scientific principles.

Electricity Is a Form of Energy. The first fact to learn about electricity is that no one—not even the ablest scientists—knows exactly what electricity is. Scientists know only that electricity is one of the several forms of energy and that it apparently exists in the form of tiny particles. Energy, as a scientist views it, is the CAPACITY FOR PERFORMING WORK. Energy can take different forms. Heat, light and electricity are three FORMS of energy. They are not different energies—they are different FORMS of the same thing. Each form of energy can be converted into any one of the other forms. Many of the processes which take place in sending and receiving radio messages and television change one form of energy into another form.

Electrons. Scientists have discovered several kinds of electrical particles. Some are charged negatively; some show no charge; others are charged positively. The negatively charged particles are called ELECTRONS. In radio, electrons are of more interest than the other kinds of particles. Some neutral electrical particles (neutral because they show no charge) are thought to be combinations of positive and negative particles.

Electric Current. A moving electron is an electric current. The electric currents used in radio consist of a large number of moving electrons. The amount of electric current represented by a single moving electron is so small that it cannot be detected by the most sensitive measuring instruments. It requires billions of billions of electrons to produce currents of sufficient strength to be useful. Approximately 5,240,093,717,045,500,000 electrons must move through the filament of the common 100-watt, 120-volt tungsten lamp each second in order to light it to full brilliance. Immeasurable billions of electrons move through the electrical wiring in your home to supply illumination for a single evening.

The Terms D. C. and A. C. The letters D. C. are an abbreviation for District of Columbia but they are also an abbreviation for DIRECT current. A current of electricity which always flows in the same direction is a DIRECT current. The current produced by a battery is direct current. So is the current from an automobile generator.

A. C. is the abbreviation for ALTERNATING current. An electric current which constantly and regularly reverses its direction of flow so that it surges back and forth in a circuit is an alternating current.

The first generating stations produced direct current for light and power. Alternating current came into use later. Alternating current can be distributed more efficiently and for greater distances that direct current. Consequently the electrical power which is produced nowadays at large generating stations and SENT OVER TRANSMISSION LINES is alternating current. The current which comes into our homes from a DISTANT generating station to provide power and light is alternating current. It usually flows in one direction, then reverses and flows in the opposite direction 60 times per second. For that reason it is called 60 cycle current. One complete flow of current backwards and forwards is called a CYCLE and the number of cycles per second is known as the FREQUENCY.

High-Frequency Alternating Currents. Electric currents can be made to alternate or reverse their direction of flow fewer or more than 60 times per second. They can be made to alternate at any rate from a few times a second to millions of times per second. Currents which alternate 100,000 times or more per second are called RADIO-FREQUENCY, HIGH-FREQUENCY and OSCILLATORY currents. The currents used to produce radio waves are radio-frequency currents. The AM waves which carry the programs of American broadcast stations are produced by radio frequency currents ranging from 550 to 1700 kilocycles. Kilo is a term derived from a Greek word meaning *thousand*. 550 kilocycles are 550,000 cycles. The waves which carry FM and television signals and also those used for radar are produced by alternating currents which reverse their direction of flow millions of times per second. They are rated in MEGACYCLES. There is part of another Greek word in this term, namely *megas*, meaning large. Meg and mega are used in science to mean MILLION. A megacycle is 1,000,000 cycles. This bit of information will enable you to understand some of the terms used in radio.

Wires, Insulators and Electric Currents. Fortunately, electric currents will not flow through all materials. Otherwise we would not be able to keep electricity under control and lead it wherever we wish. The materials through which electric currents flow most easily are called CONDUCTORS. All conductors do not carry electricity equally well. Those which conduct poorly have RESISTANCE to a current and are called PARTIAL conductors. Materials through which electric currents do not flow are called

NON-CONDUCTORS. The non-conductors used to protect the wires and parts of an electrical circuit so that current will not leak through them are called INSULATORS. Porcelain, rubber, glass, mica, waxes and Bakelite are common insulators employed in the construction of radio and electrical equipment.

The best conductors are metals and water solutions of certain chemicals. Copper is an excellent conductor of electricity. An electric current can flow through copper more easily than through any other metal except silver. Silver is too expensive to use for electrical wires except in some special instruments. Since copper costs less and conducts almost as well as silver, it is commonly employed in the form of wire to conduct electricity from place to place.

Copper wires are often covered with an insulating material to prevent short-circuits and leakage of current when wires touch adjacent objects or touch each other. Many materials are used as insulation on wires, for example, rubber, plastics, glass fiber, wax, cotton, silk and various chemical coatings.

ELECTRICAL MEASUREMENTS

Almost everything must be measured at some time or other. The measurement may be in seconds, days, weeks, quarts, gallons, pounds, tons, inches, feet or miles by some special system. Measuring is simply a means of comparison. Although electricity cannot be seen, heard or touched it can be measured by comparison to a STANDARD FOR ELECTRICITY. So also can the circuits and conductors which provide a path for electricity and harness it for some useful purpose. You will find the words volt and ampere used in this book. They are measuring units for electric current.

The Volt. Voltage is often called electrical pressure. Just as air or water flowing through a pipe exerts pressure so does an electric current exert pressure when it flows through a wire. Electrical pressure cannot be measured in pounds but can be measured by a unit called a volt. The abbreviation for volt is V.

A single dry cell, when fresh and not supplying current, has an electrical pressure or voltage of 1.5 volts. When two dry cells are connected in series the voltage is combined and amounts to 3 volts. A 45-volt B battery consists of 30 cells connected in series. An electric current requires voltage in order to overcome the resistance which it meets in conductors. A single 1.5-volt dry cell does not have enough voltage to overcome the resistance of the human skin. If you place dry fingers on the terminals of a 1.5-volt dry cell you probably will not feel any shock. There is enough voltage in a 45-volt B battery to overcome the skin resistance and give a shock unless the fingers are calloused. A 45-volt B battery has 30 times as much voltage as a single 1.5-volt dry cell and will force 30 times as much current through a circuit. The voltage of the house lighting current delivered to residences by public utilities is usually about 120 volts. 120 volts is 80 times as much electrical pressure as the 1.5-volt pressure of a single dry cell and will force 80 times as much current through a circuit.

The Ampere.   It is also necessary to have a measuring unit for the volume of flow of an electric current. It is called the AMPERE. Two amperes means a certain definite amount of electricity flowing through a circuit in one second just as 2 gallons per second indicates the rate at which water may be flowing through a pipe. A 100-watt, 120-volt incandescent lamp requires slightly less than one ampere in order to light to full brilliancy. The filament of the 1H4G radio tube used in one of the receivers described in this book requires much less current, namely 0.06 amperes.

HOW TO UNDERSTAND THE WIRING DIAGRAMS

Any of the condensers, resistors, coils, detectors, tubes, etc., which are part of the radio apparatus described in this book can be illustrated by a simple drawing called a symbol. Radio experimenters, engineers and mechanics use these symbols to make wiring diagrams or "hookups" which explain more simply than words can how to build or connect any sort of radio or electronic apparatus. Three kinds of diagrams are used to illustrate radio circuits: pictorial diagrams, block diagrams and schematic diagrams. All three will be found in this book. Pic-

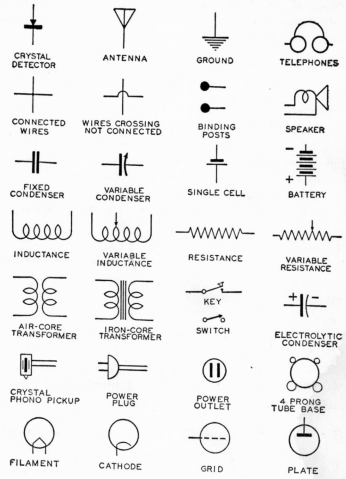

CRYSTAL DETECTOR	ANTENNA	GROUND	TELEPHONES
CONNECTED WIRES	WIRES CROSSING NOT CONNECTED	BINDING POSTS	SPEAKER
FIXED CONDENSER	VARIABLE CONDENSER	SINGLE CELL	BATTERY
INDUCTANCE	VARIABLE INDUCTANCE	RESISTANCE	VARIABLE RESISTANCE
AIR-CORE TRANSFORMER	IRON-CORE TRANSFORMER	KEY / SWITCH	ELECTROLYTIC CONDENSER
CRYSTAL PHONO PICKUP	POWER PLUG	POWER OUTLET	4 PRONG TUBE BASE
FILAMENT	CATHODE	GRID	PLATE

THE SYMBOLS USED IN RADIO CIRCUIT DIAGRAMS

Symbols are a sort of radio shorthand used to make schematic circuit diagrams. These are standard symbols used in radio books and magazines. Only those symbols used later in this book are shown.

torial diagrams are most easily understood by beginners; the condensers, detectors, transformers and other parts are readily recognized. The pictorial diagrams will help you to understand schematic diagrams. Schematic diagrams employ symbols which are a sort of radio shorthand. For example, instead of showing a drawing of a variable condenser a symbol like this —⊣⊢— is used. Notice that one line in the symbol is straight and that the other is a curved arrow. The fixed line represents the immovable plates or stator of the condenser, the curved arrow is a symbol for the movable plates or rotor.

A schematic circuit diagram of a receiver which shows the sizes of the condensers, resistors, etc., is like a plan for a house or machine. It shows how all the parts are assembled and anyone familiar with radio construction can assemble the receiver without any information other than the diagram.

When you become familiar with the symbols, you will prefer schematic diagrams.

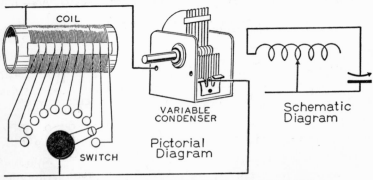

PICTORIAL AND SCHEMATIC DIAGRAMS COMPARED

Here are two methods of illustrating the same thing. Both sketches show a variable condenser connected to a tuning coil called a variable inductance. The left hand sketch is a pictorial diagram. A schematic diagram is at the right. Not everyone can draw pictorial diagrams but it is not difficult to make schematic diagrams. Radio technicians, engineers and experienced amateurs prefer schematic diagrams. Pictorial diagrams are more easily understood by beginners. Since this book is for beginners, both types of diagrams are used.

CHAPTER THREE

ABOUT RADIO WAVES

If you stand at the edge of a pond and strike the surface of the water with a stick, ripples or small waves will spread out from the spot on the surface where the stick struck. The little waves will spread in circles until they reach the opposite shore if it is not far. It would be possible to arrange a code or signals so that by counting or timing the waves they would carry a message to another person standing on the opposite shore of the pond. For example, two groups of waves, one following the other after a short interval could mean "no." In the same way, three groups of waves spaced a few seconds apart could signal "yes."

This simple arrangement whereby groups of waves carry a message illustrates the principle of radio communication. More than 50 years have passed since the first wireless telegraph message was sent and received but present day radio communication uses the same basic principles employed before the turn of the century. Broadcasting, television, radar, loran, radiotelegraphy, and radiotelephony consist of CREATING AND DETECTING HERTZIAN WAVES.

The radio apparatus now in use is vastly more complicated and much more efficient than the first radio apparatus but radio still depends upon the discovery that:

1. When a very rapidly alternating electric current flows into an antenna wire some of the electrical energy will radiate out into space in the form of Hertzian waves.

2. When these waves strike another antenna they will create therein feeble alternating currents similar to those which produced the waves.

A radio broadcast receiver changes these feeble currents into sounds; a television receiver changes them into sounds and pictures.

Radio apparatus for producing radio waves is sometimes arranged so that the waves are formed into a beam like the beam of a searchlight which can be sent in any desired direction. The radio waves used for communication between Europe

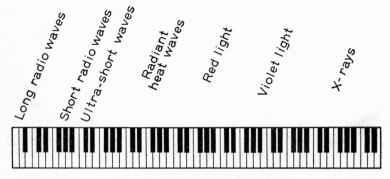

AN "ELECTROMAGNETIC WAVE PIANO"

Radio waves, light and X-rays are electromagnetic waves. The waves that produce X-rays are very short. The waves which produce light visible to human eyes are longer than X-ray waves but not so long as radio waves. If apparatus having a keyboard like a piano could be arranged so that pressing the keys would produce electromagnetic waves of different lengths, the effect could be:

When the keys at the left, or bass end of the keyboard were pressed, long radio waves would be sent into space. Pressing some of the keys to the right of the bass would produce heat. Pressing the proper key farther to the right would produce a bright red light. Other keys in the same octave would bring forth orange, yellow, green, blue and violet light. Higher up, in the treble, pressing a key would send forth X-rays.

and America and between North and South America are beamed in this manner. In the early days of wireless, the antenna was usually arranged so that the waves spread out in circles with the transmitting antenna as their center.

THE MEANING OF THE WORD RADIO

The fact that electric waves are a form of RADIANT energy and RADIATE from the antenna brought a new word into use. RADIO replaced the earlier term "wireless" and has been adopted into our language to mean "the transmission and reception of signals by means of electric waves without a connecting wire." The word "wireless" is still in use in Great Britain.

HOW ELECTROMAGNETIC WAVES ARE PRODUCED

When Hertz discovered how to produce electric waves, the waves were named Hertzian waves in his honor. This term is seldom used nowadays. The names in popular use are "radio waves" and "air waves." The term, "air waves," is often used by newspapers and radio announcers, but is a complete misnomer. Hertzian waves are not "air waves." They pass through air in moving to or from a radio station but the air is not the medium which makes their passage possible. The effect of the air on Hertzian waves is so slight that it can be ignored for practical purposes. Winds do not disturb the waves. Air which is ionized (the air molecules bear an electric charge when air is ionized) has an effect upon the path of radio waves and as we shall see later aids in long-distance radio communication.

Hertzian waves, or radio waves as they will be referred to in the remainder of this book, are ELECTROMAGNETIC WAVES. They have both an electrical and a magnetic character. Radio, light, heat, x-rays and many other effects are due to electromagnetic waves.

The apparatus for creating radio waves is called the TRANSMITTER; that which detects the waves and renders their messages intelligible is the RECEPTOR, or as it is popularly called, the RECEIVER. Radio waves are created by sending rapidly alternating currents into an insulated wire called the ANTENNA. An antenna is used also at the receiver to pick up or intercept the incoming waves.

In this instance "insulated wire" does not mean a wire covered with insulation. Antennas are usually bare wires, insulated from the earth, from their supports and from surrounding objects. However, there is a type of antenna which is known as a "grounded antenna." It is insulated in the usual manner except at a point where it is purposely connected to the earth. An antenna may consist of a single wire or an elaborate arrangement of wires. These statements do not apply to the antennas used for television, radar and the extremely short waves called microwaves.

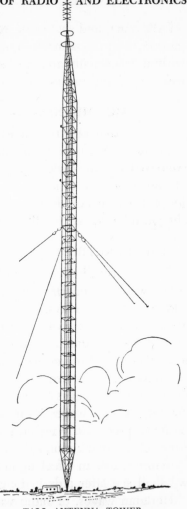

TALL ANTENNA TOWER

An antenna which is high above ground sends its waves farther over the earth's surface than a low antenna. Television and broadcasting stations use high antennas to increase the area over which the station can be heard. In some instances the antenna is supported by a steel tower 1000 feet high. Modern transmitting antennas are more efficient than the antennas used in the days of "wireless" telegraphy.

In the "pioneer days" of wireless telegraphy, the waves were produced by rapidly charging and discharging the antenna with high voltage currents from an induction coil. This method was soon replaced by better procedures for generating very rapidly alternating currents and sending them into the antenna. Transformers connected to Leyden jars or condensers, electric arcs, and alternators* were used as generators of high-frequency alternating currents for producing electric waves, but none were wholly satisfactory.

Nowadays the rapidly alternating currents which are sent into the antenna are generated by electron-tubes. Without such tubes, present-day wireless telephony, broadcasting and television would not have been possible.

RADIO WAVES HAVE LENGTH AND FREQUENCY

A radio broadcasting station is not permitted to operate unless it has a government license. Each station is licensed to send out waves of only a certain wavelength or frequency so that it will not interfere with other stations whose programs are heard in the same area. The frequency of a wave is the NUMBER OF WAVES WHICH OCCUR IN A SECOND. For example, station WABC in New York City is licensed to send out a wave having a frequency of 770 kilocycles. WNBC and WOR, both also in New York City, have assigned frequencies of 660 and 710 kilocycles respectively. Kilo means ONE THOUSAND.

When waves move along over the surface of the ocean or of a lake, the distance from the crest of one wave to the crest of the following wave is the WAVELENGTH. The distance from crest to crest of a radio wave is also its WAVELENGTH. Although radio waves are invisible, their wavelength can be accurately measured by appropriate scientific instruments. Radio waves are always measured in meters or centimeters because scientists use the metric system of meters and centimeters in preference to the English system of feet and inches. A meter is 39.37 inches

* An alternator is a dynamo for producing alternating current.

or the equivalent of 3.28 feet. A 200-meter wave is therefore 656 feet long.

There is no sharp dividing line where "long" radio waves cease to be long waves and become "short" waves. It is customary to consider "short" waves to be those with a wavelength of less than 200 meters; also that radio waves are divided into the following groups:

Ultra-short waves	10 meters and less
Short waves	10 to 34 meters
Medium short waves	34 to 200 meters
Long waves	200 to 30,000 meters

HOW RADIO WAVES BEHAVE

Radio waves travel through free space at the same speed as light waves, roughly 300,000,000 meters or 186,000 miles per second. Radio waves are much longer than light waves. They range in length from approximately 30,000 meters to a fraction of a centimeter. A meter is equal to 39.37 inches; a centimeter equals 0.3937 inches. The frequency of radio waves ranges from about 10 kilocycles to 1,000,000 megacycles. A megacycle is ONE MILLION cycles. The shortest waves have the highest frequencies.

Radio waves can be reflected and refracted like light waves. Reflected means "thrown back" like sunlight thrown back by a mirror.

When radio waves graze the edge of an object in passing, for example a hill, they tend to be bent around the edges of the object to a slight extent. This type of bending is called diffraction. Some large objects such as hills and buildings cause "radio shadows" to be formed. The waves do bend enough to enter the space behind the object and so there is a radio "shadow" there.

Another type of wave bending is called refraction. Refracted means "bent." The bending known as refraction occurs when waves move obliquely into an air mass which has different electrical qualities from the atmosphere they leave. There are changes in the electrical characteristics of the air at the boundaries between atmospheric areas of differing temperature

ELECTRONIC NIGHT SIGHT

This sailor is aiming a carbine equipped with a Sniperscope. Several thousand Sniperscopes and Snooperscopes were manufactured and delivered to U. S. military forces during World War II. These electronic instruments make it possible to see in complete darkness. They are effective up to 60 yards. Experimental models have operated effectively at distances up to ½ mile.

Electronic night sight is accomplished by picking up infra-red light invisible to human eyes and converting it into visible light.

The Sniperscope resembles a telescope in appearance. It is designed for mounting on a rifle. Thus equipped, a marksman can see his target and aim his rifle in total darkness. The device is a sort of miniature television transmitter and receiver. A pick-up camera similar in principle to the orthicon television pick-up camera forms an invisible image on the screen of the pick-up tube. A visible image then appears immediately on the screen of a special cathode-ray tube. Sniperscopes were used extensively by the Marines at Saipan, as early as December, 1944.

The Snooperscope is intended for the detection of infiltrating enemy troops and reading maps at night. One model utilizing radium in its construction is so sensitive it can detect a camouflaged tank by its engine heat hours after the motors are shut down.

Most radio and radar blind-landing apparatus is not effective in an airplane during the last 50 feet above ground. A Snooperscope could fill this gap. A possible peacetime development of the Snooperscope may provide aircraft with an electronic eye which "sees" in darkness and dense fog close to the ground.

HANDY TALKIE

This is a small, compact, light-weight portable short-wave radio telephone transmitter and receiver which was developed originally for use by the armed forces. It is now in use by policemen, firemen, sheriffs and at some sports events. If you hold one of these amazing instruments to your mouth and ear like an ordinary telephone you can talk to a person several hundred yards away via radio if they are provided with a similar instrument.

and moisture content. Refraction occurs at those boundaries.

Reflection, refraction and diffraction account for part of the behavior of radio waves.

The reflection of radio waves makes radar possible. Smokestacks, tanks, power wires, bridges, hills, mountains and many other objects reflect radio waves. The Germans took advantage of this fact during World War II and were first to shower

metal-impregnated paper strips over battle areas. Radio waves
were reflected by the metal and confused the Allied radar warning network. Later the Allies adopted the same trickery and
used showers of aluminum foil to confuse the German radars
and hide the position of Allied bombers on their way to targets
in Germany.

The reflection of waves which takes place 55 to 195 miles
above the surface of the earth has a marked effect upon radio
communications. This region, high in the heavens, where the
reflection and refraction of radio waves takes place, is known
as the IONOSPHERE. The length of radio waves and the type of
antenna from which they radiate greatly influence the path
they follow through space.

When radio waves move away from the antenna of a broadcasting station, they travel out through space by two routes.
Some have their "feet on the ground" and follow the surface
of the earth. They are called ground waves. The strength of
ground waves fades very rapidly as they move away from the
transmitting antenna. Other waves, called sky-waves, leave the
earth's surface and travel outward and upward in space. Somewhere in the upper atmosphere they meet the region of the
ionosphere which reflects and bends them so that they return
to earth again.

The short waves used in television do not follow the curva-
ture of the earth. They go forth in a horizontal line like the
light beam from a lighthouse. The path of radar waves is like
the path of the light beam from a searchlight.

The effect of the ionosphere in bending radio waves so that
they return to earth at distant points explains how low-powered,
short-wave amateur stations can communicate halfway around
the world.

RADIO STATIONS SEND FARTHER AT NIGHT

It has already been explained that ground waves quickly
become weak as they travel away from the transmitting station.

They eventually become so weak they cannot be detected. Between that point and the place where the sky-waves reach the earth there is often a "dead" area where a station's signals cannot be heard. This dead area is called the SKIP DISTANCE. The ionosphere is closest to the earth at noon and causes sky-waves to return to earth at a point closer to the transmitting station than they do at night. Radio stations can send farther at night than they can in the daytime because the ionosphere is higher and the station's sky-waves return to earth at a point which is farther from the station than it is in daylight.

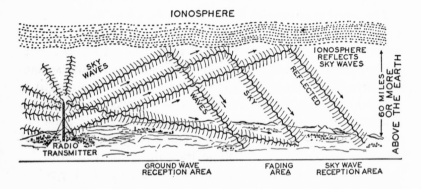

LOW-POWER SHORT-WAVE STATIONS
COMMUNICATE LONG DISTANCES BY MEANS OF SKY-WAVES

Some of the waves sent forth by a radio transmitter have their "feet on the ground." They follow the contour of the earth and are called ground waves. The strength of ground waves fades rapidly with distance. Other waves, called sky waves, travel outward and upward away from the earth. Somewhere in the upper atmosphere they meet a reflecting and refracting layer called the ionosphere. Sky waves would be of no practical use for communication purposes if they did not return to earth again. When they meet the ionosphere, sky waves are reflected back to earth at distant points where the ground-waves are too weak to be detected. Sky waves make it possible for amateurs in America to communicate with "hams" in Australia and vice versa.

CHAPTER FOUR

ELECTRONS AND ELECTRONICS

The word ELECTRONICS could not be found in the dictionary a few years ago. It is a new word, it came into our language recently; it is the name of a vigorous young science which is an important branch of electrical science. Radiotelegraphy, radiotelephony, broadcasting, television, radar, long distance telephony, sound motion pictures, public address systems are all part of the science of electronics. Electronics has many applications. At the end of this chapter is a list of the principal ones.

Electronics has become of inestimable value in modern industry and warfare. The name Electronics came from ELECTRON. All apparatus employing electron tubes belongs to the realm of electronics. Electron was originally a Greek word—the name for amber and gold. Amber was used by the ancient Greeks as a jewel and a decoration. Its yellow luster reminded the Greeks of native gold and they applied to amber the same poetic name. Today you will find amber in museums, cigar stores and jeweler's shops. It is used chiefly for pipe stems and for beads.

If you rub a piece of amber against your coat sleeve, the amber will attract and pick up tiny bits of paper, lint and thread. This property of amber was first noticed thousands of years ago. At that time spindles made of amber were used for spinning and on days when the atmosphere was dry, lint and small particles of dust were attracted to the amber. Today we know that any object which has an electric charge will do the same thing. We know that amber becomes charged with electricity when it is rubbed and that is why it often has the power to attract.

You do not need a piece of amber to see the attractive power of an electric charge. Snip some tissue paper into very small bits, about as large as the head of a dressmaker's pin. Then rub briskly with a piece of wool or fur a hard rubber pipe stem or comb or some article made of Lucite. Bring the pipe stem or comb near the paper bits slowly

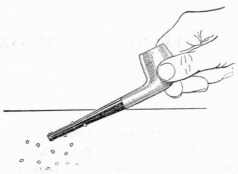

THE ATTRACTIVE POWER
OF AN ELECTRICAL CHARGE

Rub a hard rubber pipe stem with a piece of wool or fur. Rubbing will bring electrons to the surface of the rubber. The pipe stem will then have an electrical charge and will attract small pieces of tissue paper or bits of other light material. A lucite comb can be used in place of a pipe stem.

and just before it touches them some will jump up to meet it. Rubbing a rubber comb or pipe stem with wool or fur gives the surface of the pipe stem or comb a negative charge. Electrons leave the wool or fur and rest on the surface of the rubber. Electrons—you will remember—are tiny particles of negative electricity. They are invisible but scientists can easily prove their existence. Electrons were given their name in 1897 by the British physicist G. Johnstone Stoney. He was looking for a name for the tiny particles of negative electricity and he decided to call them ELECTRONS—the name the Greeks had originally given to amber. Now let us turn our attention to electron tubes.

ELECTRON TUBES

The conductors by which electric current enters or leaves a liquid, a vacuum tube or a tube containing a gas are called electrodes. An electron tube is a device consisting of a number of electrodes within a metal or glass enclosure which has been totally or partly evacuated. That last word, evacuated, in this case means emptied of its air. The operation of all types of electron tubes is dependent upon the movement of electrons within the tubes.

Sir John Ambrose Fleming invented the first electron tube for radio use. Fleming* was an English physicist and electrical engineer. He was consulting engineer to the Edison Electric Light Company of London for ten years and scientific adviser to the Marconi Wireless Telegraph Company for more than 25 years. His service with the Edison Electric Light Company brought many of the problems associated with incandescent lamps to Fleming's attention. The lamps of that time contained a filament made of carbon. As one of these lamps burned, the inside surface of the glass bulb became gradually blackened. Thomas A. Edison, inventor of the first practical incandescent lamp, noticed this effect when he was making early experiments in the manufacture of incandescent lamps. Edison also noticed that one side of the filament was gradually eaten away before the other and thus eventually burned out. In order to find the cause, Edison had carbon filament lamps built with a special metal plate inside each glass bulb. It was then observed that when the filament was lighted an electric current could be made to flow across the space between the filament and the plate. Edison was unable to explain the reason for this or to put it to any use. He made a careful record of his observation and it came to be known as the Edison Effect.

In the scientific world it is such apparent trifles that are developed into the marvels of tomorrow when they happen to

---

* BORN: November 29, 1849 in Lancaster, England. He was knighted March, 1929 for his "valuable service in science and industry."

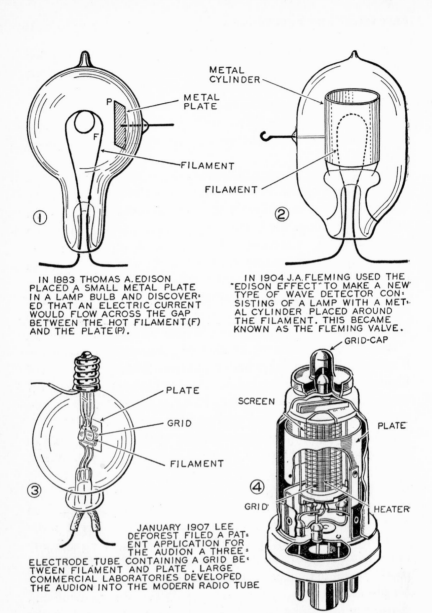

METAL CYLINDER

METAL PLATE

FILAMENT

FILAMENT

① IN 1883 THOMAS A. EDISON PLACED A SMALL METAL PLATE IN A LAMP BULB AND DISCOVER= ED THAT AN ELECTRIC CURRENT WOULD FLOW ACROSS THE GAP BETWEEN THE HOT FILAMENT (F) AND THE PLATE (P).

② IN 1904 J.A. FLEMING USED THE "EDISON EFFECT" TO MAKE A NEW TYPE OF WAVE DETECTOR CON= SISTING OF A LAMP WITH A MET= AL CYLINDER PLACED AROUND THE FILAMENT. THIS BECAME KNOWN AS THE FLEMING VALVE.

PLATE

GRID

FILAMENT

GRID-CAP

SCREEN

PLATE

GRID

HEATER

③ JANUARY 1907 LEE DEFOREST FILED A PAT= ENT APPLICATION FOR THE AUDION A THREE= ELECTRODE TUBE CONTAINING A GRID BE= TWEEN FILAMENT AND PLATE . LARGE COMMERCIAL LABORATORIES DEVELOPED THE AUDION INTO THE MODERN RADIO TUBE

④

FOUR STAGES IN THE DEVELOPMENT OF THE RADIO TUBE

excite the curiosity of the right mind. Fleming also investigated the blackening of electric light bulbs. In one of his experiments he placed a metal cylinder around the negative leg of the hairpin-shaped carbon filament inside the lamp bulb and discovered that the space between the cylinder and the filament could then be used to change alternating current into direct current.

When Fleming became electrical adviser to the Marconi Co. he gave his attention immediately to the shortcomings of the Marconi coherer and other devices used as detectors of wireless waves at that time. He began to search for a better detector—some sensitive "electrical valve" which would change the feeble, rapidly alternating currents of the receiving antenna into direct current. The thought occurred to him: "Why not try the Edison Effect?" His experiments soon proved that if a metal cylinder which enclosed the whole filament was placed inside the lamp, the arrangement became an excellent detector.

Although there was no contact or connection between the filament and the metal cylinder, electrons flowed from the hot filament to the cold metal plate. The hot filament emitted electrons, the plate collected them. Fleming named his invention an OSCILLATION VALVE and applied for a patent Nov. 16, 1904.

For several years the Fleming valve was extensively used as a detector by the Marconi Wireless Telegraph Company and the British Royal Navy. But Fleming's valve was only a radio tube in its pupa stage. It was a "two-element" or "two-electrode" tube and did not start to grow up until Dr. Lee De Forest, an American inventor, added a third element in the form of a wire grid. At first De Forest put the grid on one side of the lamp filament and a metal plate on the other. Experiment soon brought him a better understanding of his new device and he placed the grid in the center, between the filament and plate, where it belonged. De Forest named his invention the AUDION.

The audion, a three-element electron tube, proved to be a

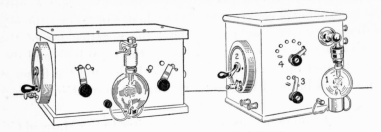

AUDION DETECTORS FOR AMATEURS

These audion detectors were placed on the market for amateur use by the De Forest Radio Telegraph and Telephone Co. at about the time Germany began World War I. The cabinets enclosed the flashlight batteries used to supply current to the plate circuit. A new audion tube could be obtained only by sending the old one back to the factory. 1, audion; 2, rheostat to control filament current; 3, switch to turn filament current on and off; 4, switch to vary plate voltage.

far more sensitive detector than its simpler two-element ancestor, the Fleming valve. In addition to being a detector the audion possessed the ability to MAGNIFY feeble currents of electricity. It was an AMPLIFIER—a new instrument destined to find a thousand uses. Undoubtedly the greatest single advance in the development of electron tubes for radio came when De Forest placed a grid in his audion between the filament and the plate.

For a time all the possibilities of the De Forest audion were not recognized and could not be utilized. The reason was that the glass bulb enclosing the filament, grid and plate of a De Forest audion was not completely exhausted of its air or gas.

Then came Irving Langmuir (in later years a recipient of the Nobel Prize in Chemistry) and H. D. Arnold, an engineer of the American Telegraph and Telephone Company. Langmuir had recently abandoned teaching at the Stevens Institute of Technology in Hoboken, N. J., to take up research work in the laboratories of the General Electric Company at Schenectady.

Each of these men began to experiment in his own way with the audion and it was not long before both discovered that the audion's behavior and dependability were greatly improved when the glass bulb was almost completely exhausted of air. The three-element electron tube became more sensitive as a detector and more powerful as an amplifier when almost all of the air was pumped out of the bulb, but it still remained only a detector and an amplifier. Until 1912 the tube still contained a secret unsuspected except perhaps by a handful of young men.

One of these young men was Edwin H. Armstrong, Professor of Electrical Engineering at Columbia University. In 1912 Armstrong, who was then 22 years of age and in the junior electrical engineering class at Columbia, made an astonishing discovery which in a few years revolutionized radio. To understand what Armstrong had discovered, bear in mind that three circuits are necessary to operate a three-element electron radio tube as a detector or as an amplifier. These circuits are: the filament circuit, the grid circuit and the plate circuit.

Young Armstrong found that an audion detector became more sensitive and produced louder signals if the grid and plate circuits were properly connected or coupled together so that current was fed back from the plate circuit to the grid circuit. He also discovered that by the same means an audion could be made a generator of alternating currents of very high frequency.

This discovery of Armstrong's is called the regenerative or feed-back circuit. It laid the foundation for almost unlimited developments in electronics which followed. Nowadays when high-frequency oscillations are sent into an antenna to propel radio waves out into space, the currents are generated by an electron tube using some form of feed-back circuit. The transmission of radiotelegraph, radiophone, radar, television and facsimile signals embody the ideas and discoveries of hundreds of men, but they all depend upon the discovery which Armstrong made in a little bedroom laboratory in his home in Yonkers, N. Y.

Armstrong patented his invention but became involved in extensive litigation with De Forest, who claimed to have made the discovery before Armstrong. De Forest won the final decision made by the courts. Judges receive a legal education, not a scientific education, and must sometimes hear highly technical testimony in patent suits, testimony which they do not understand. Many prominent scientists and radio men believe that Armstrong was actually the inventor of the regenerative or feed-back circuit in spite of the fact that a court decided De Forest made the invention a short time ahead of Armstrong.

Armstrong's career in radio was a most notable one. He made many basic inventions. He invented the superheterodyne receiver. It is the most widely used type of radio receiver. He also devised the present-day system of sending and receiving by FM or frequency modulation.

RADIOTELEGRAPHY AND RADIOTELEPHONY

The radio waves which carry the signals of radiotelegraphy, television, radar and facsimile are appropriately called CARRIER waves. The waves are produced by sending high-frequency alternating currents into an ANTENNA. Several methods of generating high-frequency alternating currents for this purpose have been used in the past but today they are almost always generated by an electron tube called an OSCILLATOR.

The same radio receiver can be used for both radiotelegraph and radiotelephone messages. An antenna is also used at the receiver. It may be a long wire, elevated in the air or, as is the case in portable receivers, a wire rolled up into a flat coil. The purpose of the receiving antenna is to intercept the waves from the transmitting station. When the waves strike the receiving antenna they produce feeble high-frequency alternating currents of the same frequency as those of the transmitting station which produced the waves. The receiver changes and strengthens the feeble currents generated in the receiving antenna so that they can produce sounds in a telephone receiver or loudspeaker.

Part of the receiver called the TUNER selects the waves from the station to be listened to and prevents interference or "jam-

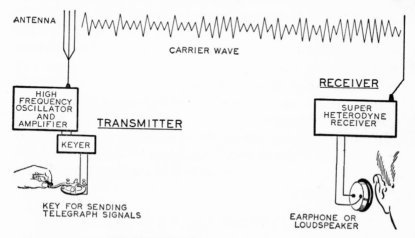

THE PRINCIPLE OF RADIOTELEGRAPHY

Radio engineers draw a rectangle (called a block) to represent intricate apparatus or machinery. This illustration and the two which immediately follow it are "block" diagrams in which complicated apparatus is represented by a rectangle. A block diagram is somewhat like an architect's plan for a house. The plan does not show all of the beams, boards, etc. A diagram showing all the details of a radio transmitter is too complicated to have much meaning to anyone but a radio engineer.

The present day radiotelegraph transmitter consists of an oscillator and amplifier, a modulator, key, antenna, a ground connection and source of power. The modulator of a radiotelegraph transmitter is usually termed a keyer. The key and keyer modulate the carrier waves produced by the oscillator and antenna by making changes in the waves which correspond to the dots and dashes of the telegraph code.

By comparing this diagram with the two which follow you will notice that the basic differences between radiotelegraphy, radiotelephony and television lie in the method of modulating or impressing the signals on the carrier waves. The ground connection on a radio transmitter may be to the earth itself or as in a radio transmitter to a metal framework or some form of counterpoise.

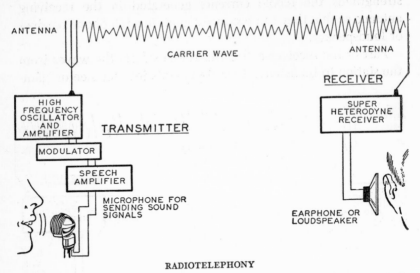

RADIOTELEPHONY

Radiotelephones and radiobroadcasting stations use the same sort of transmitter. The same type of oscillator used in radiotelegraphy is employed but a modulator controlled by a microphone is substituted for the key and keyer. Speech and music directed into the microphone modulate the carrier waves in accordance with SOUNDS instead of the dots and dashes of the telegraph code.

ming" from other transmitters which may be operating at the same time within range of the receiver.

A transmitter for radiotelegraphy is quite similar to a transmitter for radiotelephony or broadcasting. The principal difference is in the apparatus used for MODULATING the carrier waves. Modulating the waves gives them their message. It produces variations or changes in the waves which correspond to the signals or messages. At a radiotelegraph transmitter, the waves are modulated or varied to correspond with the dots and dashes of the telegraph alphabet. At a radiotelephone transmitter the waves are modulated or varied to correspond with sounds, speech and music.

The modulator of a radiotelegraph transmitter is called the keyer. It is controlled by an ordinary hand-operated telegraph key or by a tape-operated key when messages are sent at high speed.

The modulator at a radiotelephone transmitter is controlled by a microphone. Speech or music directed into the microphone modulates the carrier waves in accordance with sounds. A broadcasting station is a radiotelephone transmitter which sends out scheduled programs for public entertainment. When phonograph records are played at a broadcasting station a phonograph pick-up replaces the microphone which controls the modulator.

AM AND FM

What do AM and FM mean? AM is the abbreviation for AMPLITUDE MODULATION and FM stands for FREQUENCY MODU-

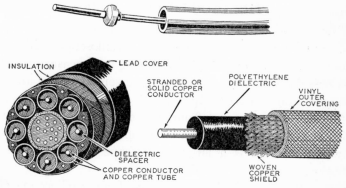

INSULATION

LEAD COVER

STRANDED OR
SOLID COPPER
CONDUCTOR

POLYETHYLENE
DIELECTRIC

VINYL
OUTER
COVERING

DIELECTRIC
SPACER

COPPER CONDUCTOR
AND COPPER TUBE

WOVEN
COPPER
SHIELD

COAXIAL CABLES

A group of television or broadcasting stations connected together to send out the same program simultaneously is called a network. The "key" station sends its program to the others in the network by coaxial cables or radio relay stations. A coaxial cable is a copper tube with a copper wire running through its center or axis. The wire is held in the center of its tube and insulated from it by ceramic or plastic spacers. The coaxial cable (lower left) which the A. T. and T. Co. installs underground between cities is a lead-covered eight-tube cable, capable of carrying 8 television or broadcast programs and more than 4500 telephone conversations simultaneously. The single-conductor cables illustrated are used in studios and transmitting stations.

LATION. These are two methods of modulating the carrier waves for radiotelephony and the programs of broadcasting stations. Many broadcasting stations send out AM and FM programs simultaneously.

Amplitude modulation is the older method. When music and speech are transmitted by this system, the STRENGTH of the waves is varied by the sounds which the microphone picks up. When they are transmitted by frequency modulation, the FREQUENCY of the carrier waves is varied by the sounds.

The system of FM in use is the invention of Prof. E. H. Armstrong. Its advantage is absence of static and noise and more faithful reproduction of sounds than is produced by AM modulation. A special type of FM receiver is required in order to pick up FM messages and programs. This type of receiver cannot be assembled by the young novice at radio building.

THE OSCILLOSCOPE TUBE

A bottle-shaped electron tube called an OSCILLOSCOPE tube made radar and television practical. Oscilloscope tubes were used originally in laboratories for testing and measuring. Other uses were soon found and it is now an essential part of all radar and television receivers. In radar it is an oscilloscope tube that measures the distance from the radar to the object or target which has been detected. The kinescope or "picture tube" of a television receiver is a large oscilloscope tube designed for television.

The bottle-shaped glass envelope of an oscilloscope tube contains:

1. An electron gun for producing a stream of electrons.
2. A fluorescent screen.
3. A device for focusing the electron beam.

The tube also includes a means of moving or DEFLECTING the electron beam up and down and from side to side. The means for deflecting the beam may be either inside or outside the tube. It is usually on the outside of the tubes used for television.

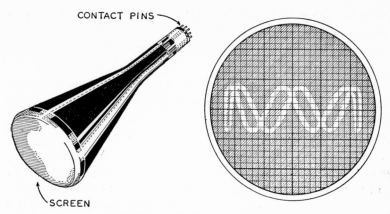

CONTACT PINS

SCREEN

OSCILLOSCOPE TUBE AND SCREEN

A laboratory device which can "paint electronic pictures" and measure time in millionths of a second. The oscilloscope screen at the right displays a fluorescent pattern produced by an alternating current. An oscilloscope tube is an essential part of radar receivers. The "picture tube" or kinescope of a television receiver was developed from the oscilloscope.

That part of the tube called the electron gun is not a Superman weapon. It was given the name electron gun because it produces a beam of electrons and shoots it at the fluorescent screen at the opposite end of the tube. The gun consists of a heater and a cathode, similar in principle to the heater and cathode in the tubes in your home radio receiver. The heater resembles the filament of an incandescent lamp—it becomes hot when an electric current passes through it. Its purpose is to heat the cathode. The cathode is made of metal which has been treated with a chemical that produces many electrons when heated. The electron gun is built into the neck of the tube.

The fluorescent screen is a thin coating of phosphors on the inside surface of the large end of the tube. Phosphors are chemicals which glow when struck by electrons. The fluorescent screen glows wherever the electron beam strikes it. The air is pumped out of the tube and a small amount of argon introduced before the tube is sealed. The argon aids in concentrating the electron beam so that where it strikes the screen a small glowing spot results.

When an oscilloscope tube is in operation the electron beam may be deflected up or down or sideways. When the beam is at rest, it produces a small glowing spot on the fluorescent screen. When the beam is moved, it makes a luminous line on the screen—a line which may be either curved or straight—depending upon the manner in which the beam moves. The glow in the phosphors on the screen dies away quickly when the electron beam moves away but the pattern drawn by the beam can be kept there as long as necessary by causing the beam to constantly repeat its movements.

The electron beam is focussed and deflected by electrical charges applied to metal plates built in the oscilloscope tubes made for laboratory work and for some radars.

R-A-D-A-R

The British called it radiolocation but the U. S. Navy named it RADAR as the abbreviation for "Radio Detection and Ranging." Radar uses radio waves to detect the presence and character of objects beyond the range of human eyes.

Radar was the most important element in winning the battle of Britain and a large factor in the Allied victory over the Germans and Japanese. This new miracle of science warned the British of the approach of German bombers before the latter could be seen or heard. Fighters were then sent on the proper course to intercept them. Thus the pursuit planes of Britain's pitifully small Royal Air Force were able to concentrate quickly at areas in immediate danger of bombing by the enemy. Often they were alerted in time to meet the Luftwaffe over the Channel and ward off the impending blow. Radar coupled to an efficient bombsight enabled American and British bombers to pound Germany from the air almost daily in both good weather and bad. The "black box" which was a combination radar and bombsight made it practical to bomb ground

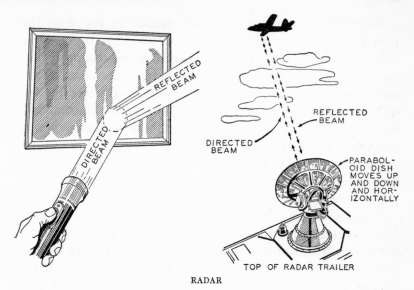

RADAR

A radar station sends out its radio waves in the form of a beam which can be pointed in any direction like the beam of light from a flashlight. In the same way that a mirror struck by a beam of light reflects it back, so objects struck by a radar beam reflect it back to the radar station. Noting the direction of the radar beam and measuring the time which elapsed between sending out a "pulse" and the arrival of its echo indicates the exact location of a reflecting object even though it may be hidden by clouds or darkness or be beyond the range of human vision.

targets through clouds. When the earth was obscured by night or clouds an image which was a reproduction of the ground below appeared on the screen in the box. Water showed up as a dark patch, objects such as ships, houses, etc., appeared as lighter spots. American warships equipped with radar spotted and sank Japanese warcraft which were otherwise invisible because of darkness. Naval battles fought at night near Cape Esperance and Guadalcanal were costly defeats for the Japanese because our cruisers opened fire without first disclosing their presence through the use of star shells and flares.

When German submarines were destroying the ships that kept England alive and supplied our overseas troops radar helped to wipe out the underwater peril. Radar-equipped ships and airplanes were able to discover submarines miles away— by day or night. Radar had been so perfected before the end of the war that it not only located the enemy but automatically aimed and fired anti-aircraft and naval guns with superhuman accuracy. Although radar was developed entirely for war, it is not solely a tool of combat. It is saving many lives in peacetime applications. Its use aboard planes and ships and at airports increases the safety of travel.

Mounted in the cab of a locomotive, radar enables the engineer to detect other trains on the same track. Vessels provided with radar can sail into a harbor during heavy fog without colliding with other ships. At sea, radar warns of icebergs, floating wrecks and other ships. Aboard an airliner, radar gives pilots an accurate picture of their altitude at all times. It reveals such hazards as tall buildings, mountains, other planes, radio antenna, smokestacks and high tension wires. It will assist a plane to a safe landing in a dense fog.

No one man invented radar. It is largely the work of many research teams. Radar had its beginning before World War II but its great development took place during the war. Radar was first discovered in the United States in 1922. Scientists working for the Radio Division of the U. S. Naval Laboratory observed that the signals from a radio station were interfered with by objects moving in their path. So they set up a radio receiver on the banks of a river to study the effects on signals caused by boats passing up and down the river. With the knowledge gained from these experiments development work was immediately begun on apparatus for detecting ships passing between harbor entrances, or between ships at sea. The plan called for a transmitter and a receiver at different locations.

In 1925 the apparatus was redesigned to have both the transmitter and the receiver at the same location. It made use of the fact that many objects act as reflectors of radio waves. The radio signals sent out by the radar transmitter were made to strike the target and then bounce back to the receiver.

In 1930, the apparatus had been developed sufficiently to pick up waves reflected back from planes passing overhead. Four years later a means of measuring the distance between the radar transmitter and the target was added.

The manner in which radar operates is more easily understood if you bear in mind that radio waves are reflected when they meet an obstruction.

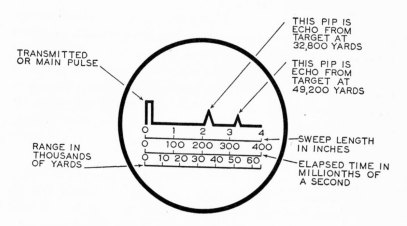

SPLITTING A SECOND INTO A MILLION PARTS

The oscilloscope tube is the "heart" of a radar receiver. When in operation, a radar transmitter sends out waves only a very small part of the time. Its waves are sent in intense bursts of short duration called pulses. An oscilloscope tube measures the time it requires for the pulses to travel to a target and return as echoes. The outgoing pulses produce a "pip" on "scope" screen and so do their echoes. If the electron beam in the scope screen sweeps across the screen for a distance of one inch in 1/10,000th of a second: a distance of 2 inches between the pulse's pip and its echo's pips indicates that the echoes come back from an object 32,800 yards distant. The screen on the radar scope is graduated with fine lines so that the position of pips shows at a glance the distance of a target. A radar scope tube can be arranged to present its information in different ways. That illustrated above is called A-scan presentation.

The radar transmitter and receiver are located at the same place. The transmitter sends out its waves in very intense bursts of small duration called pulses. Each pulse may last only a millionth of a second. After each pulse the transmitter waits a few thousandths of a second before sending out the next pulse and during that interval the receiver listens in.

The wave pulses sent out by the transmitter are focussed by the antenna into a beam which can be pointed in any direction like the beam of light from a searchlight. The beam is moved by electrically operated machinery. It moves over the entire region to be searched. Travelling at 186,000 miles a second, the wave pulses go out into space, never to return unless they strike an interfering object. In the same manner that a mirror struck by a beam of light from a flashlight reflects it back, so do reflecting objects such as ships, airplanes, water tanks, prominent buildings, mountain tops, etc., bounce back the radar wave pulses. The radar receiver located near the transmitter

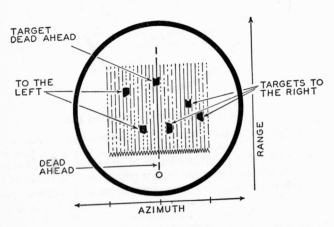

THE SCOPE SCREEN
IN A RADAR-EQUIPPED FIGHTER PLANE

The screen on a scope for B-scan presentation shows a fighter pilot the location of other planes which may be flying in the region up to 90° on either side of dead ahead. It also shows their distance.

detects these echo waves which bounce back. Near-by objects give echoes very soon after the outgoing wave pulses leave the antenna; objects farther away give echoes which arrive later. The time which elapses between sending a pulse and receiving its echo measures the distance of the object which is producing the echo. The intervals between pulse and echo are very short —they are measured in millionths of a second. Their exact measurement is one of the great technical achievements of radar. An object 2000 yards from a radar transmitter produces an echo which arrives at the receiver only three millionths of a second after the outgoing pulse left the transmitter. But the radar measures this with such accuracy by using the time interval as an indicator of the distance that there is an error of only 15 or 20 feet.

You may wonder how the direction of the object or target is determined. The antenna which sends out the beam of wave pulses moves constantly up and down and around so as to

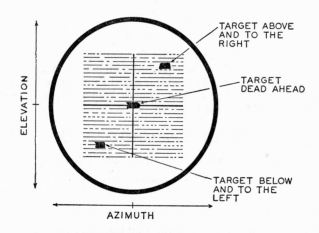

THE SCOPE SCREEN
IN A RADAR-EQUIPPED FIGHTER PLANE, *continued*

C-scan presentation indicates planes ahead and whether they are to the right or left and above or below.

thoroughly search an area. The strongest echo comes back when the beam of pulses sent out by the radar is pointed directly at the target. By noting the direction of the wave beam and measuring the time which elapses between sending out a pulse and the arrival of an echo from that pulse, the exact location of the target or reflecting object becomes known even though it may be hidden by clouds, distance or darkness.

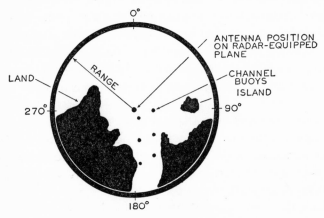

RADAR IN A BOMBER

In addition to a scope which indicates the position and distance of other planes and targets, bombers are equipped with a scope which presents a map of the area being searched. This is called PPI-scan presentation and is used for search, harbor control, convoy keeping, ground controlled interception, navigation and bombing.

THE RADAR PROXIMITY* FUSE

An ingenious device called the radar proximity fuse was one of the super-secrets of World War II. Until it was invented there was no way to insure that an anti-aircraft shell would explode at the right spot. It might burst before it reached its target or some distance beyond. The ordinary fuse on an artillery shell can be set to explode the projectile at a certain TIME after the shell is fired. Before the shell is loaded into the gun,

* Proximity is the state of being near or very close.

an artilleryman sets the fuse so that the shell will burst a definite time after it is fired and hopes that the timing is correct so that the shell bursts close to its target. A proximity fuse is not pre-timed. Its projectile bursts only when it NEARS an object. Its burst is controlled by proximity to a target, not by timing.

The proximity fuse is a miniature self-powered radio transmitter and receiver no larger than a pint milk bottle. It is enclosed in the nose of the projectile. It operates on radar principles. When the shell is fired from a gun, the proximity fuse starts sending out its radio wave. When the projectile gets within 70 to 100 feet of a plane or other target, the waves are reflected back to the miniature receiver in the fuse. The reflected waves are a signal that the shell is close to an object. The receiver amplifies the signal and feeds it into an electron tube called a thyratron. The thyratron acts as a power switch and explodes the projectile at the right spot, close to the target. Four miniature electron tubes are used in each proximity fuse. It was no simple task to put such delicate parts into a projectile and have them operate dependably. When fired from a gun, the fuse must withstand the shock of a change in velocity from 0 to 2,000 miles per hour in a distance of 10 feet. But the problem was solved successfully.

MARINE RADIO BEACONS

Radio first contributed to safety at sea by providing telegraphic communication between ship and shore. Every mariner and every person who travels on the sea recognizes radio's aid to safety. It has been the means of saving the passengers and crews of many disabled, sinking or burning vessels, which, without radio, would probably have been listed simply as "missing." Rescues at sea, where aid was summoned by radio, are headlined in the newspapers and the whole world soon knows about them. But all the world does not know that radio is working quietly and constantly to PREVENT marine mishaps.

Accurate time signals and weather warnings are regularly broadcast over the entire ocean area to give mariners a frequent check on their chronometers (the clocks used in calculating a ship's position) and on weather conditions. In addition, there are approximately 200 radiobeacons on the coasts of the U. S. A. Radiobeacons are an important aid to navigation. They enable vessels to check their positions by radio.

Radiobeacons are radio stations which send out radio signals in all directions to guide marine navigators. They are operated by the United States Coast Guard. The beacons are installed at lighthouses, on lightships and at other points shown on the marine maps called charts which navigators use. In this country, radio signals are sent out from the beacons for 1 minute

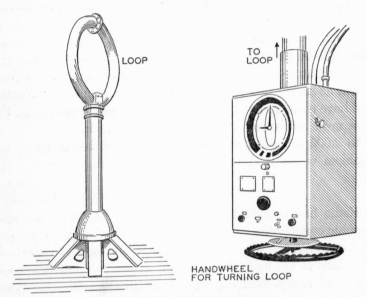

RADIO DIRECTION FINDER

The antenna connected to the receiver of a radio direction finder consists of a coil of wire enclosed in a waterproof casing. The loop (left hand sketch) is mounted above decks or on the roof of the pilot house. The loop can be rotated by a hand wheel on the receiver. The receiver (see right sketch) is usually located in a cabin directly below the loop.

out of each 3 minutes and for one or two 10-minute periods each hour during periods of good visibility. When there is fog and when visibility is low, the radiobeacons send their signals continuously. The signals, on wave frequencies of 285 to 325 kilocycles, are short and simple combinations of dashes and dots which the station repeats without variation. Each beacon has its own signal, different from that of all other beacons and is easy to identify.

A ship must be equipped with a radio direction finder in order to check her position by the signals of the radiobeacons. The direction finder is simple and comparatively inexpensive. many yachts and fishing boats are equipped. The device is an ordinary radio receiver connected to a loop antenna arranged for observing the DIRECTION of any station sending radio signals.

The loop antenna is a large coil of wire which is usually mounted above the ship's pilot house. It is fastened to the upper end of a movable shaft which extends downward into the pilot house. The lower end of the shaft is provided with a handwheel and an indicator over a compass. The navigator or observer can rotate the loop by turning the handwheel. If the loop is turned, the indicator also moves.

To use the direction finder the navigator first picks up the signals of a radiobeacon with the receiver. Then he turns the loop and notes how the signal strength varies as the loop is rotated. He continues to turn the loop until a point is reached where the signal is lost entirely or nearly lost. This is called "observing the minimum" and at this point the navigator notes the position of the indicator above the compass. The indicator is connected to the loop antenna in such a manner that when the "minimum is observed" the indicator points directly to the radiobeacon and shows its compass direction from the ship. By ascertaining the direction of two or more radiobeacons whose signals can be heard by the ship, and marking lines on a chart which show their direction, the ship's position is indicated. For example, a ship approaching New York can pick up radiobeacon signals from Fire Island, Ambrose Lightship and Barnegat Lightship. When the "minimum is observed" for each of these beacons, lines are drawn on a chart showing the direction each beacon lies from the ship. The point where these lines cross each other is the position of the ship.

The most powerful foghorn signals under favorable conditions may be heard 10 to 15 miles but their usual dependable range is only 5 miles. During storms it is less. Coast lights are visible for 15 to 20 miles and large lighted buoys for 9 to 12 miles in good visibility. Radiobeacons have a much greater range of usefulness both in fog and clear weather than foghorns and lighthouses or lightships. Radiobeacons vary in power but many of them are reliable up to 200 miles. A few high-power beacons have a range of 400 miles.

LORAN

Radiobeacons are an aid to navigation for medium distances. Loran is a long range aid and is more accurate. It is not affected by changes in the position of cargo booms, ventilators, etc., as direction finders sometimes are.

The name "Loran" was coined from the words "LOng RAnge Navigation." The Loran system is an electronic aid which enables a navigator to determine the position of his ship accurately and quickly, either day or night and under practically all weather conditions. Loran signals are sent out 24 hours per day and cover the major ocean shipping lanes of the world. The effective range extends 750 nautical miles during the day and 1400 miles at night. A ship's position can be determined in 2 or 3 minutes time by Loran in clear weather or foul. A navigator needs clear skies to find the position of his ship by a celestial observation on the sun or stars with a sextant. The accuracy of an observation by Loran is comparable to that which may be expected from good celestial observations. Loran has an accuracy of better than 1 per cent of the distance of the ship from the Loran stations. Thus, a ship 500 miles away

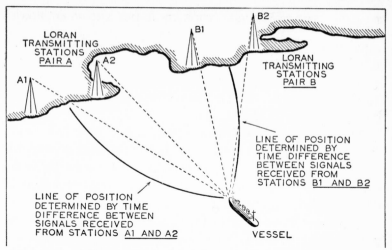

VESSEL DETERMINING HER POSITION BY LORAN

from the stations would expect her Loran equipment to indicate a position well within 5 miles of the proper position.

Loran is used by airplanes as well as ships.

Loran operates on the following principles:

1. Radio waves which carry signals consisting of short pulses are transmitted from a pair of shore-based transmitting stations. The waves are radiated in all directions and are not sent out in the form of a beam like radar waves. One of the pair of transmitting stations known as the "master" sends out each of its pulses before the corresponding pulse from the second or "slave" station.

2. The pulse signals are received aboard the ship or plane by a Loran radio receiver known as a receiver-indicator. The receiver performs in the same manner as an ordinary radio receiver but is connected to a visual indicator, an oscilloscope, instead of a loudspeaker. In this respect it is similar to a radar receiver. The oscilloscope and its equipment is essentially an "electronic stop-watch" which measures in MILLIONTHS of a second the difference in times of arrival of the pulse signals from a "master" station and its "slave."

3. The measured time difference is then used to determine from special tables or charts a line of position on the earth's surface for the ship or plane.

4. Two lines of position are secured from two pairs of Loran transmitting stations. When these lines are marked on a chart, the point where they cross each other is the Loran "fix" and indicates the ship's or plane's position on the earth's surface.

TELEVISION

When you watch a baseball game or other programs on a television receiver, you are looking at pictures which are painted by electrons. The pictures begin in a camera at the television studio or at the scene of action and are completed in the receiver. A television camera is not the sort of camera used for making snapshots. It has a lens but no film. It is an electrical camera. The first practical television cameras were called ICONOSCOPES. The name means IMAGE VIEWER; "Eikon" in Greek meaning image and "Skopon" to watch. Vladimar Kosma Zworykin invented the Iconoscope and named it. Dr. Zworykin was born in Mourom, Russia, July 30, 1889. He arrived in America in 1919 and became an American citizen. He achieved his Ph.D. in 1926 with the thesis "The Study of Photoelectric Cells and Their Improvement." Dr. Zworykin invented the Iconoscope while employed in the Westinghouse Electric and Manufacturing Company's research laboratory, "Miracle Hill," at Pittsburgh, Pennsylvania. Shortly thereafter he left the employ of the Westinghouse Company and began extensive research and development of television apparatus at the Radio Corporation of America's laboratories.

The Iconoscope has been greatly improved since its invention by Zworykin. The result is a television camera called the Image Orthicon. The cameras in use today (1954) in television are image orthicon cameras. An image orthicon is more elaborate than an iconoscope and its operation is difficult to describe in simple language. For that reason you will find an explanation of the Iconoscope below instead of a description of the image orthicon.

The cameras at a television transmitter correspond to the microphones at a broadcasting station. They pick up pictures and change them into electrical impulses; microphones pick up sounds and change them into electrical impulses. An Iconoscope is a sort of electronic eye. It is very sensitive and it sees an entire picture quickly, as a human eye does. And like a human eye, it has a memory. If you look at something and then close your eyes you imagine that you still see the object for a short time after your eyes are closed. The Iconoscope has similar "persistence of vision." It can retain a scene for a second or two if necessary.

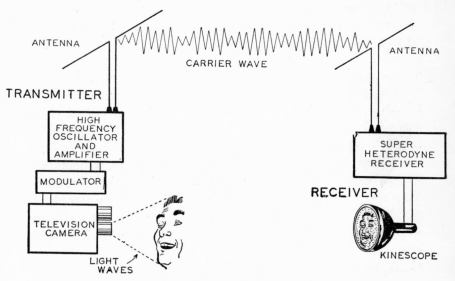

THE PRINCIPLE OF TELEVISION

This diagram illustrates the video or picture portion of a television transmitter and receiver. The audio or sound apparatus is like that used in radiotelephony. The principal difference between a video transmitter and a broadcast transmitter is that light variations instead of sound variations modulate the video carrier waves. The waves are "given their picture" by a modulator controlled by a television camera.

What the Camera Does.   The images seen on the screen of a television receiver come into the camera at the transmitter through a lens like the lens in a photographer's camera. There similarity ends, for the pictures are not focussed on a photographic film; they are focussed on an ingenious electronic screen. They form there a miniature image of the scene on which the camera is focussed. The screen in an Iconoscope is called a MOSAIC. It is a man-made electrical version of the retinas in our eyes. It is made of a thin sheet of mica which is coated with a film of metal on one side and covered on the other side with millions of tiny silver globules. The globules are microscopic in size. Each of them is a small photo cell—sensitive to light. When light strikes the globules, they become electrically charged. Those globules which are in the lighter areas of a picture focussed on the screen become more charged than the globules in the darker areas.

THE ICONOSCOPE IN ACTION

An electron gun is also an essential part of an Iconoscope. It is the same sort of electric gun that is used in an oscilloscope or in a kinescope. It shoots out a narrow beam of electrons like a water pistol squirting out a stream of water. Dr. Zworykin has called the electron beam in an Iconoscope the "optic nerve of television." He has also likened it to a "paint brush" that plays upon the "electric retina" or mosaic screen in the Iconoscope. Electronics engineers say that the beam "scans" the screen. If you look up "scan" in the dictionary you will find that one of its meanings is to examine point by point or to scrutinize. That is exactly what the electron beam does. Starting at the upper left-hand corner of the screen, it swings horizontally across the mosaic, swings back to the left and repeats this motion. Each time the scanning beam sweeps across the screen, it moves a little farther down on the image. This downward and horizontal motion of the beam is continued until the beam reaches the bottom of the mosaic screen. Then it suddenly jumps back to the top and begins its scanning again. The amazing thing is that the beam silently and invisibly swings across the screen from left to right 525 times in covering the screen from top to bottom. Thus it divides a picture into 525 horizontal lines, or we might say, the electron brush paints a picture with 525 horizontal brush strokes. Each trip down the screen it paints

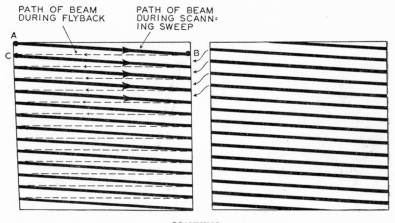

SCANNING

The Iconoscope does not view a whole picture instantaneously and a Kinescope does not reproduce a whole picture instantly. Both must go through the process called scanning in which the electron beam examines or produces one little section at a time. The electron beam moves from left to right at a slight slant when a picture is being transmitted or formed and then flys back to the left at almost instantaneous speed. An image is scanned or reproduced in two operations. The paths of the electron beam during the first pass are interlaced with the paths of the beam in the second pass. The sketches above show the two passes. If one of the sketches is placed on top of the other the heavy black lines representing the left to right swings of the beam will interlace.

every other line and when it jumps back to the top to begin its journey again it scans or fills in the lines it omitted on the last trip. The beam scans the screen from top to bottom 60 times a second. In other words, it paints 30 complete pictures every second.

When the electron beam swings back and forth over the mosaic screen it discharges the individual silver globules, that is, it causes them to lose their electrical charge. The individual globules are charged to various degrees by the light and dark portions of the picture. Discharging the globules forms a con-

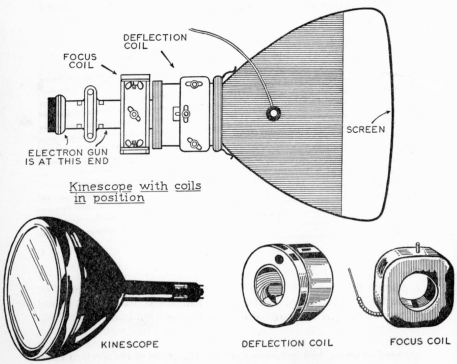

KINESCOPE OR TELEVISION PICTURE TUBE

The Kinescope is a cathode-ray oscilloscope built for the special purpose of producing television pictures. The scopes used for radar and laboratory work are similar in principle but smaller. The focus coil focusses the electron beam; the deflection coil moves the beam.

tinuous stream of electrical impulses and these constitute the "picture" or "video" signals. The video signals are sent into a video amplifier where electron tubes increase their strength. "Bewildering," you may say if you do not understand television. But it is really quite simple as well as wonderful.

Television Transmitter. Television broadcasting is carried on at ultra-high frequencies. The very short carrier waves from a television transmitter cannot be picked up by a receiver located beyond the horizon. The range of a television station is therefore limited to short distances in comparison with the range of a radio broadcasting station. That is why so many television transmitter antennas are located atop The Empire State Building. A high antenna transmits farther than a low one.

The radio transmission of television is quite similar to radio sound transmission. The transmitter which broadcasts the television pictures is called the video transmitter. The strengthened picture signals from the video amplifier go into a video modulator. There they modulate the video oscillator circuit which produces the video carrier waves. Three signals usually go out on the carrier waves a fraction of a second apart. Two of them control the horizontal and vertical movements of an electron beam at the receiver; the other varies the intensity of the electron beam and controls the black, white and halftone areas of the picture which is reproduced on the screen at the receiver. Sound usually accompanies the pictures, so a separate audio or sound broadcasting transmitter is usually included with the television transmitter.

Television Receiver. A television receiver detects and amplifies the audio or sound signals and feeds them to a loudspeaker. It also detects and amplifies the control and video signals from the video transmitter.

Kinescope. The amplified video signals are fed to a special form of oscilloscope developed by Dr. Zworykin and called a Kinescope. The Kinescope produces the transmitted pictures. The name means "to watch movement"; "Kinema" meaning movement in Greek and "Skopon" to watch.

The large funnel-shaped envelope of the Kinescope has an electron gun at the small end and a fluorescent screen at the large end. The electron gun shoots a slender beam of electrons at the screen and the screen fluoresces wherever the electrons strike. The signals that originate at the television transmitter cause the beam to scan the screen of the Kinescope in perfect step with the electron beam in the Iconoscope at the transmitter. Both beams move in the same direction at the same time. The intensity impulses that originate in the Iconoscope cause the intensity of the beam in the Kinescope to vary and paint fluorescent pictures on the Kinescope screen. This is all done silently and without any moving machinery. In case you are not duly impressed by the amazing ingenuity of a television transmitter and receiver, here is one more fact. The transmitter sends out about 5,000,000 IMPULSES EVERY SECOND in order to make the picture which you see on the Kinescope screen.

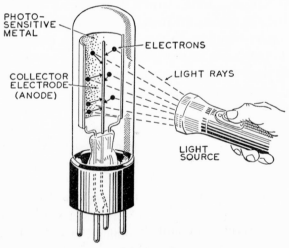

PHOTO-SENSITIVE METAL

ELECTRONS

COLLECTOR ELECTRODE (ANODE)

LIGHT RAYS

LIGHT SOURCE

PHOTOTUBE

When light rays strike the photosensitive metal in the tube, electrons are thrown off from the metal. The electrons (represented by black dots in the sketch) are collected by the anode. When electrons move from the sensitive metal to the anode, current flows in the tube circuit. This current can be amplified and made to operate a relay or other devices.

PHOTOTUBES

A tiny beam of light can be arranged so that if you intrude upon it, it will "see" you and open a door for you, or if you are an intruder it will sound an alarm. This is accomplished with an electron tube. It has already been explained that the flow of electrons in all radio tubes is controlled by means of voltages applied to the grid or plate. There is another very important class of electron tubes in which the flow of electrons is CONTROLLED BY LIGHT. These tubes are popularly called "electric eyes." Their technical name is PHOTOTUBE or PHOTOCELL. A phototube will respond to changes in the strength of light a thousand times more rapidly than human eyes can and will detect much smaller changes in the light strength. Phototubes make talking motion pictures possible, also television. A phototube will automatically turn on lights when the sun goes down. It will turn them off again when the sun comes up. It will watch for smoke and ring a fire alarm if any appears. Phototubes are used in burglar alarms, in animal traps, to count people, automobiles or other objects which pass a given point, to control automatic machines and printing presses, to bring elevators level with the floor when they stop and in many kinds of laboratory and control equipment.

Phototubes utilize the discovery that when light falls on any one of a number of substances, electrons are emitted by that substance. The production of electrons in this manner is known as the photoelectric effect. The photoelectric effect was discovered by Heinrich Hertz in 1887. Hertz never heard of electrons but he noticed that an electric spark would jump across a longer gap if the light from another spark was allowed to fall on it. Hertz was unable to find any use for his discovery but he recorded it so that it came to the attention of other scientists. In following years many men investigated photoelectric effect and contributed the knowledge which made it possible to build phototubes.

In general appearance, a phototube resembles the common

radio tubes used in a radio receiver. There is more than one type. The illustration shows a No. 929. It contains two electrodes sealed in a glass bulb. The electrodes are connected to contact pins which project from the plastic base. The air is pumped out of the bulb before it is sealed. In a No. 929 tube, known as a gas phototube, a small amount of argon gas remains. The half cylinder visible inside the tube is one of the electrodes. It is the photosensitive cathode and is made of a thin sheet of copper which has been silver plated. The silver is covered with a layer of cesium oxide and the cesium oxide is covered

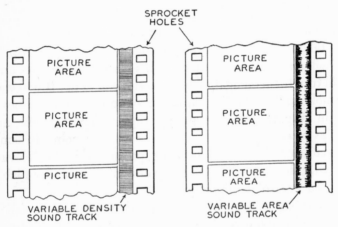

THE SOUND TRACK ON 35-MILLIMETER
MOTION PICTURE FILM

Sound is recorded on a motion picture film in the form of sound track. Two types of sound track are in general theatre use. The film at the right has variable area sound track, that at the left has variable density sound track.

Both types of sound track on film are produced photographically. A microphone picks up the sounds to be recorded and changes the sound vibrations into electrical impulses. The impulses are amplified by electron tubes fed into an optical valve which causes a beam of light to fluctuate. The fluctuating beam is focussed on the film alongside the pictures. When the film is developed the sound track appears. When the film is run through the sound head on a motion picture projector the original sounds picked up by the microphone are reproduced.

in turn with a layer of the rare silvery metal cesium. The plate electrode or anode of the tube is the small rod in the center.

A phototube may be connected with a battery and a sensitive relay so that variations in the light will open or close the relay. The relay may be arranged to ring bells, blow horns, open doors, stop and start motors, or to control any sort of device or machine. A phototube may also be connected to an amplifier and the amplifier in turn to a loudspeaker as in talking motion pictures.

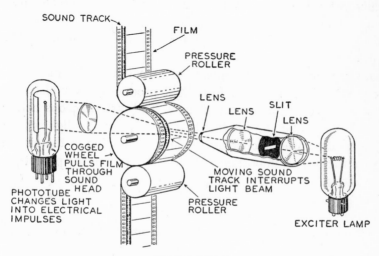

DIAGRAM OF A
MOTION PICTURE REPRODUCER SOUND HEAD

The sound head plus an amplifier and loudspeaker reproduce the sounds recorded photographically on motion picture film. In the sound head a narrow beam of light from a small brilliant incandescent lamp called the exciter lamp is focussed on a phototube. The light beam passes through the sound track on the picture film before it reaches the phototube. As the sound track moves through the beam, variations in the light and dark areas cause the light reaching the phototube to fluctuate. These light fluctuations correspond to the sounds recorded on the track. They cause the electrons emitted in the phototube to vary. The phototube is connected to an amplifier system which magnifies the variations in the electrons emitted in the phototube. The amplifier provides enough power to operate a loudspeaker located behind the picture screen.

The positive terminal of the battery in circuit with the photo-tube is connected to the anode of the tube. When light falls on the cathode of the tube, electrons are given out from it instantly. The technical way of saying this is, "When light falls on the cathode of the tube electrons are emitted instantly." The electrons flow across the space between the cathode and the anode and continue to do so long as light remains on the cathode. When electrons stream across from the cathode to the anode, current flows in the tube circuit. This happens practically instantly. When no light strikes the cathode, no electrons leave it and no current flows in the circuit. The number of electrons emitted from the cathode is dependent upon the intensity of the light which strikes the cathode. An intense light produces more electrons than a weak light and more current flows in the circuit. Less light produces fewer electrons and results in smaller current flow. The instantaneous action of the phototube and the fact that a change in the light which falls on the cathode changes the current flowing in the circuit are of the utmost importance in the many uses of the phototube in talking motion pictures, television and industry.

PIEZOTRONICS

When certain crystalline materials are pressed or twisted they generate electricity. The electricity produced in this manner is called PIEZO electricity and the crystals which produce it are called Piezo-electric crystals. The Greek-derived word "piezo" means *press* or *squeeze*. Piezo-electricity is literally "pressure-electricity." Piezo, plus the word "electronics" is the name of a new field in science. We come into contact with its developments every day of our lives.

Piezo-electric crystals have another remarkable property. If a piezo-electric crystal is placed between two metal plates and the plates are charged electrically, the crystal will change in width, in length or in thickness.

Some of the substances whose crystals have marked piezo-electric qualities are tourmaline, topaz, fluorospar, sugar, ammonium dihydrogen phosphate, Rochelle salt, lithium sulfate, quartz, dipotassium tartrate and potassium dihydrogen phosphate. The last six substances mentioned furnish the crystals which are used most frequently in piezotronics. Of these, Rochelle salt and quartz are used most extensively.

Pierre Curie, the famous co-discoverer of radium, and his brother Jacques discovered the piezo-electric effect of crystals in 1880. Their discovery remained a mere laboratory curiosity and was not put to practical use until World War I. Then quartz crystals became an essential part of submarine detection equipment. Soon thereafter quartz crystals were adopted in radio communications to control the frequency of transmitters. A

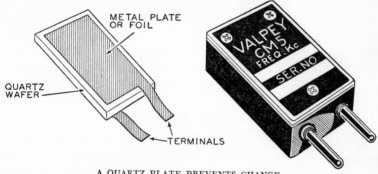

A QUARTZ PLATE PREVENTS CHANGE
IN THE FREQUENCY OF A RADIO TRANSMITTER

The quartz is placed between two metal electrodes and enclosed in a plastic case as in the right-hand sketch.

radio transmitter must be provided with an automatic governor to keep its frequency from changing. Although the piece of quartz used for this purpose is called a crystal, it is not a whole crystal. It is only a section of a crystal cut in the form of a flat plate. When the quartz plate is placed between two metal electrodes to which an alternating current is applied, the quartz vibrates and produces piezo-electricity. The pulses of piezo-electricity produced by the quartz vibrations act as pacemakers. Their frequency controls the frequency of the radio transmitter. The frequency at which the quartz vibrates depends upon its thickness. If it becomes necessary to change the frequency of a radio station, it is also necessary to connect a different quartz crystal in circuit.

Grinding quartz crystals so that they will vibrate at a definite frequency is an important branch of the radio industry.

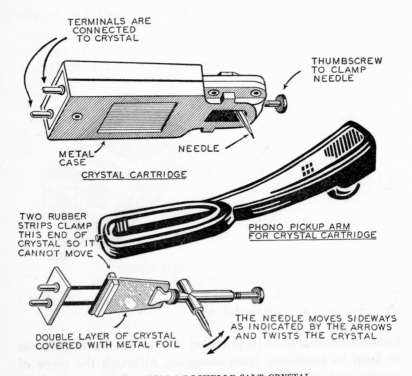

TERMINALS ARE CONNECTED TO CRYSTAL

THUMBSCREW TO CLAMP NEEDLE

METAL CASE

NEEDLE

CRYSTAL CARTRIDGE

TWO RUBBER STRIPS CLAMP THIS END OF CRYSTAL SO IT CANNOT MOVE

PHONO PICKUP ARM FOR CRYSTAL CARTRIDGE

DOUBLE LAYER OF CRYSTAL COVERED WITH METAL FOIL

THE NEEDLE MOVES SIDEWAYS AS INDICATED BY THE ARROWS AND TWISTS THE CRYSTAL

MUSIC FROM A ROCHELLE SALT CRYSTAL

Piezo crystals are in common use in phonograph pickups. Movement of the needle as it follows the groove in a record twists two plates cut from a crystal of Rochelle salt. The twisting creates pulses of piezo-electricity which are amplified and led to a loudspeaker. The two plates of crystal are clamped together. The double layer is called a "Bimorph."

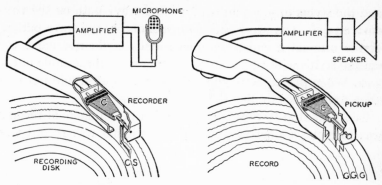

PIEZO-ELECTRIC CRYSTALS BOTH RECORD
AND REPRODUCE

When an original wax recording is made sounds directed into a microphone connected to an amplifier produce electrical pulsations that cause a Bimorph (C) to move. A cutting stylus (CS) attached to the Bimorph cuts the wax. This action is reversed when a record is played. A needle (N) attached to a Bimorph twists the crystal as the needle point follows the wavy groove (GGG) in the record. The piezo-electricity generated by the crystal is fed to an amplifier. A loudspeaker connected to the amplifier changes the electric currents into sounds.

MODERN PHONOGRAPH RECORDS ARE MADE AND PLAYED BY "PRESSURE ELECTRICITY"

The coming of radio sent the old hand-cranked phonograph to the attic. It came back into the living room again a few years later as the modern record player. The change and improvement were brought about by developments which had been made in electronic amplifiers and piezotronic systems.

Phonograph records are made by pressing a vinyl plastic into metal molds called stampers. Until about 1920 the process was begun by making an "original" recording on a revolving wax-covered disk. The energy which cut the wax was only the energy of sound waves. Original records were made by directing the sounds into the large end of a horn. The small end of the horn was closed by a diaphragm bearing a cutting stylus. Sounds directed into the horn caused the diaphragm to vibrate and the stylus to move and cut a spiral wavy path on the wax-covered disk. The wavy path corresponded to the wave pattern of the original sounds but some sounds could not move the cutting stylus with enough force to cut an exact facsimile in the wax. When played back, the original recording would not produce sounds exactly like the original ones.

The next step toward the production of commercial records was to make a "master" record. The original wax record was

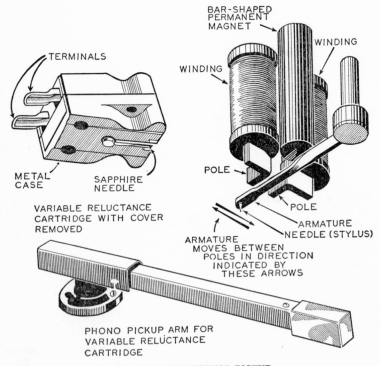

VARIABLE RELUCTANCE PICKUP

All phonograph pickups do not utilize piezo-electricity. A variable reluctance pickup generates electric currents in somewhat the same manner that a dynamo generates currents. Movement of the phonograph needle or stylus varies the amount of magnetism which passes through two small windings. Variations in the magnetism generates currents which are amplified and fed to a loudspeaker.

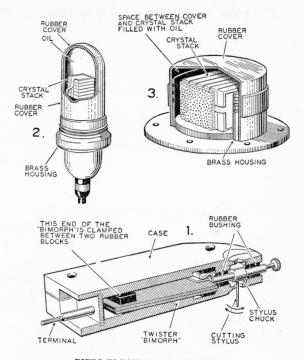

PIEZO-ELECTRIC TRANSDUCERS

1. This is a piezo-electric crystal "cartridge" used for cutting records. In the illustration, the side of the cartridge is shown cut away so as to reveal its internal arrangement. The curved arrows represent the side to side motion of the cutting stylus produced by the twisting movements of the Bimorph.

2. This is a Sonar Transducer of the type called a hydrophone. It employs a piezo-electric element to convert electrical energy into sound energy and vice versa. It will perform both as an underwater microphone and as an underwater speaker. Part of the rubber cover is shown cut away in the sketch in order to reveal the crystal stack. This consists of several thin plates of lithium sulfate crystal stacked together with interleaved parallel connected foil electrodes. When the transducer is connected to a source of alternating current, the ends of the plates have a piston-like action. The flexible rubber casing of the hydrophone is filled with oil so that the movement of the crystals is communicated to water through the oil and the waterproof rubber cover. By the same means, sound waves in the water reaching the hydrophone are communicated to the crystal stack.

3. This is a typical transducer for depth finding systems. The side of the housing and rubber cover is shown cut away so as to reveal the crystal stack. Several thin plates of Rochelle salt or ADP form the crystal stack.

electroplated with a thin layer of gold and copper. This thin metal shell was then stripped off the wax and backed by a solid metal plate. This "master" was used to produce a "mother" or several "mother" records in the case of a hit record. The "stampers" or molds used to press the records shipped to music stores were made from the "mother" by an electroplating process.

Electronics has greatly improved the fidelity of modern recordings. Today the original recording is made on magnetic tape and is a much more faithful recording than the old sound-powered recording in wax. The tape recorder is then connected to an amplifier which in turn operates a record cutter. The record cutter engraves the sounds recorded on the tape onto a lacquer disk in the form of a wavy groove. The cutter is electrically powered and all the energy necessary for the cutting stylus is provided. Its power is not limited to the energy imparted to a small diaphragm by sounds. A common type of record cutter consists of a cutting stylus attached to a piezo-electric crystal. The faintest sounds recorded on the tape result in amplified electrical impulses which cause the piezo-crystal to move and move the stylus. Since a piezo-electric crystal connected to an amplifier moves a stylus with much more energy than a sound-powered diaphragm it cuts a more faithful original recording. The metal "master" is made by electroplating the lacquer original. The master is used to produce one or more metal "mothers." Metal stampers made from the mother are used to press out the commercial records from "biscuits" of vinyl plastic.

ULTRASONIC AND SUPERSONIC

Sound can be two things:
1. the sensation produced in the ear by vibrations.
2. energy produced by vibrations or alterations in pressure.
   Most of the sounds which we hear are produced when air is

set into vibration, usually by some vibrating object which is in contact with the air.

Until a few years ago sound had limited uses. It provided our principle means of communicating with each other, in the form of music it furnished entertainment. Sounds within the body other than the sounds of the voice were sometimes of significance in diagnosing an illness. The sounds produced by a machine were often an indication to a trained mechanic whether the machine was in good working order or not. World War II stimulated research and development of other uses for sound. Sound became involved in almost every type of communication system used in the War. More recent research has found countless new and useful applications for sound.

The words ULTRASONIC and SUPERSONIC are used in both science and industry.Ultrasonic is a term used to designate sounds whose vibrations are so rapid they cannot be heard by human ears. Ultrasonic sounds vibrate more than 20,000 times per second. Young people with normal ears can usually detect sounds vibrating from 20 to 20,000 times per second. In general, when sound vibrations are less than 20 per second or more than 20,000 per second they are inaudible to human ears. Middle-aged and elderly people have usually lost the ability to hear the high-pitched sound of 20,000 vibrations per second, in fact they cannot usually hear sounds above 16,000 vibrations per second.

Webster's Collegiate Dictionary 1950 makes no distinction between SUPERSONIC and ULTRASONIC. Both terms have been used interchangeably in the past to designate high-pitched sounds above the range of the human ear. Lately, the term SUPERSONIC has acquired new meanings. The word has been adopted, particularly by the Air Force and others, to refer to the speeds of objects moving in air faster than the speed of sound. Many engineers and books on acoustical engineering* use SUPERSONIC as the term for extremely INTENSE sounds regardless of their frequency.

* An acoustical engineer is an engineer whose field is the science of sound.

Intense sound energy produced by supersonic and ultrasonic generators can be used to bring about desirable changes in gases, liquids and solids. These include homogenizing milk, jarring the dirt out of clothes, clearing the atmosphere of smoke, fog and dust and discovering invisible flaws in steel. The Sperry Products Co., manufactures an ultrasonic device whose sounds penetrate solid metal and locate unseen flaws. Hundreds of these devices are used in manufacturing plants and railroad shops to find and locate faults in machinery. Doctors are experimenting with a somewhat similar ultrasonic instrument to locate shell fragments and tumors and to detect gallstones.

Ultrasonic waves under careful control pass harmlessly through the soft tissues of the body but echo back when they strike more solid objects. Ultrasonics have been used successfully to pulverize gallstones in dogs and rabbits. It is possible that this method may someday replace surgical operations to eliminate gallstones from human beings.

The energy of ultrasonics does such a perfect job of mixing ingredients that many factories use it for mixing chemicals, paints, soft drinks, cake batters, medical preparations, etc. Oil and water can be blended so effectively that they cannot be separated again for years. When jarred by the energy of supersonics many molten metals that would never mix together heretofore can now be blended into useful alloys.

Transducers. Ultrasonics are produced by a "transducer" or "converter of energy." A microphone, which converts sound energy to electrical energy, a loudspeaker which converts electrical energy to sound energy, and a photocell, which converts light energy to electrical energy may be given the general name of transducers. However, they are not the transducers used to create ultrasonics. A piezo-electric crystal, connected to a vacuum tube oscillator, is a simple and efficient transducer for creating ultrasonics. A vacuum tube oscillator and amplifier are arranged to produce alternating currents which alternate from a few times per second to millions of times per second. When electrical energy from this source is fed to a piezo-electric transducer, the transducer produces sounds whose vibrations have the same frequency as the alternating current.

UNDERWATER SOUNDS
HELPED TO WIN WORLD WAR II

A submarine which is cruising on the surface can send and receive radio messages like any other ship, but a submarine's radio equipment is useless when she is completely submerged. The reason for this is: radio waves are rapidly weakened in passing through sea water. Sea water is a good conductor of electricity. Fortunately water of any kind is a good medium for the transmission of sound waves and consequently sound can

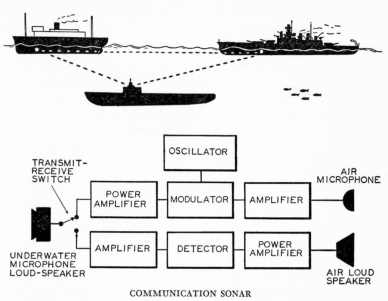

COMMUNICATION SONAR

Underwater sound waves are used to telephone and telegraph from ship to ship, particularly by submerged submarines. In general, the same underwater transducer is used as both a loudspeaker and microphone. A switch connects the transducer to either the transmitting apparatus or the receiver.

be used for underwater communication. A method of sound signalling called SONAR is almost universally used for underwater communication. The term SONAR was recently added to our language. It was coined from SOund Navigation And Ranging. Sonar embraces all types of underwater apparatus used aboard ships for underwater communication between

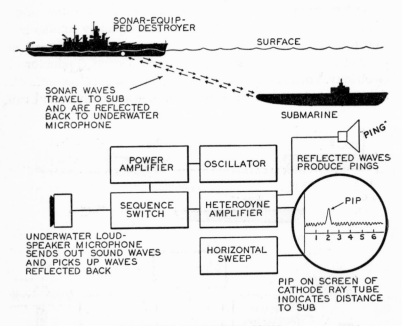

DIRECTION AND RANGING SONAR

The presence and location of a submerged submarine may be determined by SONAR. The principle is the same as that of RADAR with this difference: sonar utilizes sound waves, radar uses radio waves. A short pulse of 25 cycle alternating current is sent into the underwater transducer. The transducer sends out sound waves. The sequence switch immediately disconnects the transmitter and connects the receiver to the transducers. If any of the sound waves are reflected back by the hull of a submerged submarine, the transducer acts as a microphone and picks them up. The reflected or echo waves produce a "pip" on the screen of an oscilloscope tube and a "ping" sound from the air loudspeaker. The position of the pip on the scope screen indicates the distance of the submarine.

ships, whether they are surface ships or submarines. It includes also apparatus for depth sounding, for navigational aid and for locating and tracking submarines.

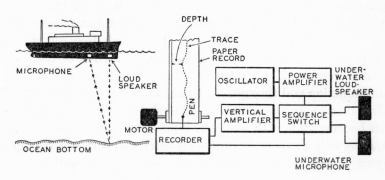

ECHO DEPTH FINDING SONAR

It is no longer necessary for a seaman to drop a weighted line into the water to find its depth. Depths from 5 feet to several thousand feet may be measured instantly by the sonar equipment of a ship. An underwater transducer is mounted flush with the hull of the vessel and directed downward. A short pulse of high frequency alternating current (10 to 100 kilocycles) sent into the transducer produces sound waves which travel to the bottom and are reflected back. When a pulse is sent, the sequence switch immediately connects the transducer to a recorder. The sound of a reflected pulse causes a pen on the recorder to make a dot on a moving strip of paper. The process is repeated every few seconds. Graph paper calibrated in fathoms is used on the recorder so that the position of the dots made by the pen indicate the depth of the water below the ship.

X-RAYS

The discovery of the invisible penetrating light called X-rays gave us an instrument of inestimable value for healing physical injuries and treating disease. It provided a window of the body through which the trained specialist can look to see that which heretofore had been hidden from his eyes. X-rays are produced when electrons travel at high speed and strike a metal target in a special form of vacuum tube. They were discovered by William Konrad von Roentgen, Professor of Physics at Wurzburg, Germany. Here is how Roentgen found X-rays:

In the early 1880's, Professor William Crookes, an English physicist, constructed some peculiar pot-bellied vacuum tubes. He pumped part of the air out of some of the tubes. Other tubes he connected to a special vacuum pump which drew out almost all of the air so that only an infinitesimal fraction of the original air remained. When he passed a high voltage current from an induction coil through his tubes, Professor Crookes noticed that those which contained a comparatively large amount of air became filled with luminous light and that those tubes containing only a FEW molecules of air acted DIFFERENTLY. No light glowed within a high vacuum tube but its glass wall became

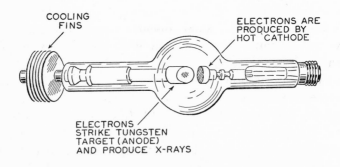

COOLING FINS

ELECTRONS ARE PRODUCED BY HOT CATHODE

ELECTRONS STRIKE TUNGSTEN TARGET (ANODE) AND PRODUCE X-RAYS

A MODERN X-RAY TUBE

For a long time X-ray tubes were unreliable. The vacuum inside the glass bulb had a tantalizing way of changing. A tube which would work satisfactorily one day would not necessarily do so on the day following. Then out of the laboratories of the General Electric Company came an improved tube named after its inventor, Dr. William D. Coolidge. The making of X-ray pictures with the dependable Coolidge tube became almost as simple as the taking of ordinary photographs. Until the Coolidge tube was devised all X-ray tubes had a cold cathode. Coolidge type tubes contain a hot cathode, heated by a filament. The hot cathode furnishes electrons more freely than a cold cathode.

fluorescent with a strange greenish-yellow light. Some sort of
invisible ray which came from the negative electrode (cathode)
in the tube struck the glass and caused the pretty fluorescence.
Crookes called the unknown rays CATHODE RAYS. He was amazed
when he found that the rays would bend under the influence
of a strong electromagnet brought near the tube. "It is radiant
matter," he said, "which is striking the glass." As this great
scientist gazed in awe at the cathode-rays he had discovered,
he was unaware that he had just missed discovering X-rays
and the electron.

About twenty years elapsed before it was known why the
glass wall of a high-vacuum Crookes tube glowed while the
space within remained dark. In the autumn of 1895, Professor
von Roentgen connected a large induction coil to a Crookes
tube. The tube was completely covered with a closely fitting
layer of black cardboard. When the apparatus was operated in
a completely darkened room, Roentgen made an astonishing
discovery. A paper screen coated with some compounds of
barium and platinum lying near the tube lighted up brilliantly
with a fluorescent glow. The fluorescence was observable when
the screen was six feet away from the apparatus. Such a weird
happening had never been noticed before. Roentgen soon con-
vinced himself that the invisible agency which caused the
fluorescence originated at the point in the tube where its glass
wall was struck by the cathode rays and that it had passed
through the layer of cardboard covering the tube.

Upon further experiment he found that this invisible ray
would pass through many substances which were opaque to
ordinary light. It would go through stone, through thin layers
of metal, through living flesh and would affect a photographic
plate. The behavior of the new invisible rays was so puzzling
that Roentgen could not decide whether they were a form of
light or a sort of vibration, so he adopted the symbol used in
algebra for an unknown quantity and called them X-RAYS.

Electronics has many applications. Here are the principal ones:

ENTERTAINMENT

Radio broadcasting
Television broadcasting
Studio recording
Program pickup stations
Booster stations
Home radio receivers
Home television receivers
Amateur radio
Amateur radar
Amateur television
Phonographs
Recorders
Sound motion pictures

COMMUNICATIONS

Radio, telegraph and telephone to ships and other countries and vice versa
Radio teletype
Radio telephone and telegraph from ship to ship
Submarine cable booster and repeater equipment
Telephone repeater stations
Telephoto transmission of pictures
Facsimile
Police radio
Taxi radio
Truck radio
Railroad radio
Citizens' radio
Air-ground communications
Navigation by radio and radar
Airplane traffic control
Airplane Instrument Landing

INDUSTRIAL ELECTRONICS

Automatic control devices for machines
Automatic power distribution
Inspection in factories
Quality control in factories
Electronic timers
Electronic computers
Color matching
Heating
Soldering
Exploration for minerals and oil
Electronic instruments for testing and measuring
Weather observation instruments

CYCLOTRONS FOR ATOM SMASHING

ATOMIC ENERGY ELECTRONIC EQUIPMENT

MEDICAL ELECTRONICS

X-ray equipment
Diathermy
Electron microscopes
Electrocardiographs and other instruments for diagnosis

MILITARY ELECTRONICS

Radio telephone and telegraph
Radio teletype
Radio facsimile
Weather observation
Radio and radar air and marine navigational aids
Air warning radar
Fighter control radar
"Snooperscopes" for seeing in the dark
Gun and bomb control radar
Guy-laying equipment

MILITARY ELECTRONICS *(Continued)*

Guided missiles
Proximity fuses
Mine detectors
Identification
Radar bombing
Gun-sighting equipment
Submarine detection

CHAPTER FIVE

RADIO TUBES—
FEEDBACK AND REGENERATION

For less than one dollar you can buy a marvelous scientific device—namely a "tube" for a radio receiver. This inexpensive creation of scientific research does its work with a precision and a certainty that are astonishing. Not all radio tubes cost so little. Several hundred different types are manufactured. They are used in the electronics industry as detectors of radio waves, as rectifiers (a rectifier acts as a valve and thereby changes alternating current into direct current), relays, switches, amplifiers of voltage and current and as generators of alternating currents. When used for this last named purpose, a tube is termed an OSCILLATOR. Tubes are designed so that they are most efficient for one particular purpose. For example, a tube which is the best detector of radio waves is not the best amplifier and vice versa.

The electron tube, popularly spoken of as a "radio tube," is truly the "heart" of modern radio. Carefully made estimates indicate that there are 900,000,000 to 950,000,000 radio tubes in active use devoted to entertainment (broadcasting and television) and 50,000,000 in use in industry and commerce. They range in size from tiny "acorn" tubes which are about the size of your thumb nail and the sub-miniature tubes used in hearing aids to the large water-jacketed transmitting tubes termed "bottles" which are sometimes five feet high. Materials from every corner of the earth are required in manufacturing electron tubes.

When tungsten, certain other metals and metallic oxides are heated to high temperature in a vacuum they yield large numbers of electrons. This simple method of producing electrons makes it possible to build the electron tubes used in radio. A radio tube consists of a cathode which supplies electrons when heated and one or more additional electrodes mounted in an evacuated glass bulb or metal shell. The bulb or shell is termed the "envelope" in scientists' language. The additional electrodes control and collect the electrons supplied from the hot cathode.

The wonderful accomplishments of radio tubes are the result of their ability to control almost INSTANTLY the movement of millions of electrons supplied by the cathode and to do this with the expenditure of only an infinitesimal amount of control energy.

DIODES, TRIODES, ETC.

Tubes having two electrodes or elements like the original Fleming valve are still employed in radio. They are called DIODES and are used as detectors and as rectifiers of alternating currents.

The audion which Lee De Forest invented is a three-electrode tube or TRIODE. Its three electrodes consist of a CATHODE, a GRID and a PLATE or ANODE. The third electrode, or grid, is all important because it is the CONTROL electrode. The electrical charge on the grid controls the electrons in their flight from the cathode to the plate. When the grid has sufficient negative electrical charge it repels electrons and blocks their flow across the space between the cathode and plate. On the other hand, if the grid has a positive charge, it attracts electrons and increases their flow from the cathode to the plate. When a triode goes to work in a receiver, amplifier, etc., electrical charges on the grid cause the tube to fulfill its purpose.

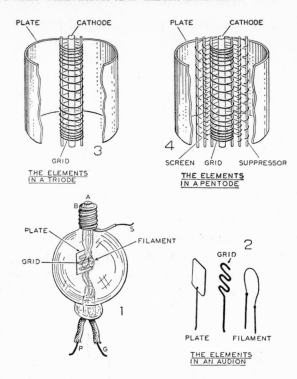

PLATE   CATHODE

GRID

THE ELEMENTS
IN A TRIODE

PLATE   CATHODE

SCREEN   GRID   SUPPRESSOR

THE ELEMENTS
IN A PENTODE

PLATE

GRID

FILAMENT

GRID

PLATE   FILAMENT

THE ELEMENTS
IN AN AUDION

RESEARCH IMPROVED RADIO TUBES

1. Modern radio tubes are far more efficient than the original De Forest audion (lower left). 2. The three elements of the audion consisted of a loop-shaped filament, a flat grid and a small flat metal plate. 3. The grid in a modern triode is usually a spiral wire which completely surrounds the cathode, and the plate is a metal cylinder or oval surrounding the grid. 4. Many modern tubes have more than one grid; tetrodes have two, pentodes have three. The cylinder plates in the illustrations above are shown cut away to reveal the grids and cathodes.

For a few years after the audion was invented, triodes were the only electron tubes used in radio, but the coordinated efforts of engineers and craftsmen have resulted in many improvements. For example, it was discovered that tubes with more than three electrodes would perform better in some circuits. Consequently, many of the tubes used in radio receivers today have five electrodes. They are called PENTODES. Tubes with four electrodes are called TETRODES. *Di, tri, tetr* and *pent* are from Greek words meaning respectively "two," "three," "four," and "five." *Diode* means "two electrodes," *triode* means "three electrodes" and so on, the name of the tube thus revealing how many electrodes are inside its glass bulb or metal shell.

MULTI-UNIT TUBES

Tubes with the electrodes of more than one tube enclosed in the same bulb or shell are called multi-unit tubes.

TWO KINDS OF CATHODES

The cathode in a radio tube does not supply electrons unless it is hot. An electric current is used to heat the cathode. A filament-cathode or directly heated cathode is a wire heated

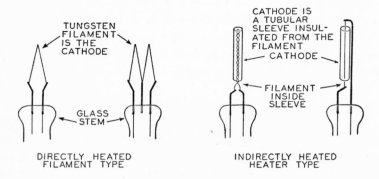

TWO KINDS OF CATHODES

The filament serves as the cathode or electron emitter in radio tubes designed for operation on direct current (left). The cathode, in tubes designed for alternating current, is separate from the filament but is heated by it. The filament of an AC tube is termed a "heater." The cathode supplies electrons when its temperature is raised sufficiently by the heater.

by the passage of an electric current. A heater-cathode, also called an indirectly heated cathode, consists of a wire filament called a heater enclosed in a metal sleeve. The passage of an electric current through the heater causes it to become hot and heat the sleeve. The outside surface of the sleeve carries an electron-emitting material which supplies electrons when the sleeve becomes hot.

The two types of cathodes each have a special purpose. Directly heated filament-cathodes require comparatively little heating current. They are used in tubes designed for battery operation in order to impose as small a drain as possible on the batteries. Directly heated filament-cathodes respond very quickly to fluctuations in the heating current. With each fluctuation there is a change in the number of electrons released. Consequently, they cannot be used on alternating current without producing a "hum" in the circuits.

Heater-cathodes are used in tubes designed for operation on alternating current. The filament in this type of cathode does not supply any useful electrons—it is used only to heat the sleeve. The sleeve does not respond quickly to changes in the heat produced by the filament and therefore there are no rapid fluctuations in the electron supply which would cause a hum.

OUTSIDE AND INSIDE A RADIO TUBE

Hundreds of radio tubes of different sizes, characteristics and purposes are manufactured by the tube makers. These are listed in catalogs or booklets which contain a basing diagram and a description of each tube. The RCA Receiver Tube Manual (price $1.00) is considered the standard list of tubes for amplifiers, radio receivers and television receivers. It contains data on current types as well as information on discontinued types in which there still may be some interest.

All electronic apparatus, employing electron tubes, must be wired so as to comply with the basing diagrams. Every young

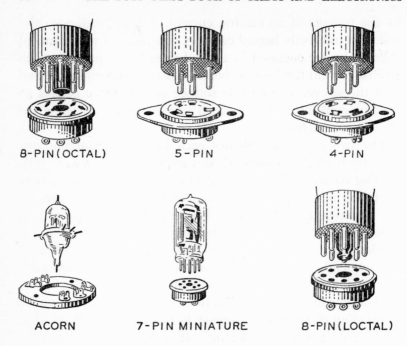

8-PIN (OCTAL)   5-PIN   4-PIN

ACORN   7-PIN MINIATURE   8-PIN (LOCTAL)

THE BASES OF RADIO RECEIVING TUBES
AND THEIR CORRESPONDING SOCKETS

electronics experimenter must learn how to interpret tube
basing diagrams. The illustration on page 95 provides the basing diagram for an 1G4/GT tube. This tube is no longer manufactured but is illustrated and discussed here because of its
simplicity. The 1G4/GT is a triode designed to be a detector or
a voltage amplifier in small battery-operated receivers. It is
simpler to describe and understand than a multi-unit tube.

The lower end of the glass envelope which encloses the elements of an 1G4/GT tube is cemented in a molded plastic base.
Seven contact pins extend from the underside of the base. The
elements in the glass envelope are connected to these contact
pins. The numbered circles in a basing diagram represent the
pins. Two of the pins (Nos. 2 and 7) on an 1G4/GT are con-

nected to the terminals of the filament. They are also marked F and F in the diagram. The filament serves as the cathode in a tube designed for battery operation. The grid and plate of an 1G4/GT are connected to pins 5 and 3 in the diagram. 5 and 3 are also marked G and P (abbreviations for "grid" and "plate"). Pins marked NC, in this case pins Nos. 1, 4 and 8, have nothing connected to them.

The mirror-like surface which may be present on the inside of tubes having a glass envelope results from a chemical called a "getter" used in producing a high vacuum. Only about 1/100,000,000 of the original air in the tube remains. A high vacuum makes receiving and amplifier tubes more efficient. Even minute traces of air, if left in a tube, would interfere with the electrons which pass across the spaces between the elements.

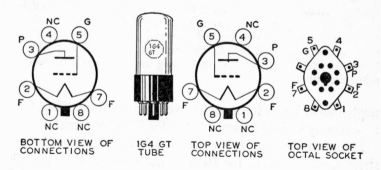

BOTTOM VIEW OF CONNECTIONS   1G4 GT TUBE   TOP VIEW OF CONNECTIONS   TOP VIEW OF OCTAL SOCKET

BASING DIAGRAMS AND SOCKET FOR 1G4/GT TRIODE

The elements in a radio tube are connected to contact pins which project from the bottom of the tube. Diagrams of this type show which element is connected to which pin. The numbered circles represent the pins.

TUBES FOR HIGH FREQUENCIES

When radio tubes are used in circuits which operate at the higher frequencies, certain properties of the tubes which were

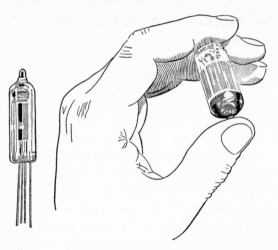

VERY HIGH FREQUENCIES REQUIRE SMALL TUBES

The elements—cathode, grid, plate, lead-in wires, terminals, etc.—in a radio tube have an electrical quality called capacitance. This effect is objectionable in many circuits, especially those designed for very high frequencies. The capacitance of a tube can be reduced by making the tube and its elements small. Small tubes have less capacitance, weigh less and take up less space. Small size tubes called miniature and sub-miniature tubes are used in receivers designed for very high frequencies. Small tubes are also useful in small light-weight receivers, amplifiers and other electronic devices. The amplifiers in hearing aids are equipped with sub-miniature tubes.

negligible at lower frequencies become important. Therefore it is necessary to build special tubes for high frequencies.

Miniature Tubes. It is customary to use miniature tubes in short wave receivers for frequencies below 200 megacycles. Miniature tubes are used also in many receivers designed for the medium frequencies. These small tubes are about ¾-inch in diameter and are all glass tubes which are called ACORN tubes because of their shape. No base or contact pins are used on an acorn tube. Connections are made directly to the electrode leads where they project from the side of the tube.

Lighthouse Tube. This tube was designed to overcome the effects of leads to the electrodes on high frequencies. Short, heavy metal rings are used instead of leads. The electrodes are as small as possible and are spaced close together so that it takes little time for the electrons to travel from the cathode to the plate. Its physical appearance gave the tube its name.

Cavity Magnetron. The most efficient radar makes use of very high frequencies. Tubes with a grid cannot be used as oscillators to produce the extremely high frequencies which create the microwaves employed in radar. One of the milestones in electronics was the development of a mysterious radio tube in 1940 at the University of Birmingham, England. It solved the problem of producing microwaves (radiowaves 50 centimeters and shorter). It made microwave radar practical for the first time. Called "maggie" by radar operators, its proper name is cavity magnetron. "Maggie" was a super secret during World War II. Microwaves enabled the Allies to inflict many devastating surprises upon German and Japanese armed forces. In appearance a cavity magnetron bears no resemblance to the common radio tube. It is a special form of diode which operates under the influence of a strong magnet, hence the name magnetron. The magnet causes the electrons which are emitted from the cathode to move in a spiral path before they reach the anode. The cavity magnetron consists of a cylindrical cathode surrounded by a massive copper anode. The anode has several keyhole-shaped cavities cut in it. The electrons emitted by the cathode are whirled in the cathode chamber past the slots in the anode by the action of the magnet. As the electrons spiral past the cavities, they cause the electrons in the cavities to oscillate in much the same manner as the air in a bottle is made to oscillate and whistle by blowing a stream of air across the mouth of the bottle.

The remainder of this chapter explains more fully the action of a radio tube. It may be uninteresting to readers who happen to be more concerned with building radio apparatus than with the principles of electronics. To many it may be difficult to understand. If you find it so, skip it. Turn to the next chapter. For the lads who wish to make radio a permanent hobby or who have great scientific curiosity, here is an explanation.

First, it should be stated that it is not difficult to explain the action of an electron radio tube to an engineer or to anyone who understands the mathematical curves called graphs which are used by engineers. But it is not possible to give a simple and at the same time complete technical explanation of the action of an electron radio tube with words only. Without graphs, the explanation is not wholly accurate because it is not complete. Graphs have been omitted because they are too technical for this book.

To make the explanation as clear as possible it is necessary to begin by repeating certain facts which have been stated elsewhere in this book.

A three-electrode vacuum tube containing a cathode (producer of electrons), a plate (collector of electrons) and a grid (controller of electrons) is called a triode. The grid is a screen or lattice-like affair containing openings through which electrons may pass. Many vacuum tubes contain more than one grid. The behavior of multigrid tubes is in many respects similar to that of a triode. A triode is simpler, easier to understand. We will explain it.

The THREE circuits which are necessary in order for a triode to play its part in a radio receiver are shown in an illustration nearby. The tube represented is the filament-cathode type which operates on 1.5 volts. It has long been the custom to call the battery which supplies current to the filament, the "A" battery and to call the battery which supplies current to the plate the "B" battery.

When a radio tube is in action one of the fundamental laws of electricity is at work. It is that:

Negative charges of electricity REPEL negative charges and positive charges REPEL positive charges, but positive and negative charges ATTRACT each other.

Electrons are tiny particles of negative electricity and in obedience to the above law are ATTRACTED by a positively charged electrode and REPELLED by a negatively charged electrode.

With this knowledge we can get a mental picture of the fundamental action which takes place when the tube is operating.

When the B battery is properly connected in the plate circuit, the positive terminal of the battery is connected to the plate and the negative terminal of the battery to the cathode. This results in a charge of positive electricity on the plate.

As soon as the A battery connected to the cathode heats the latter to sufficient temperature an invisible group of tiny particles forms close to the cathode. The invisible group is a group of free electrons, a group of tiny particles of negative electricity, which have broken through the surface of the cathode.

The velocity of the electrons as they emerge from the hot cathode is very low and they do not have energy to travel far unless they are assisted. They tend to stay close to the cathode or return to it unless they are coaxed away. Since the plate is charged positively it attracts electrons. If the grid has no charge

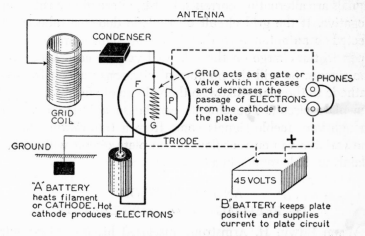

THE CIRCUIT OF A TRIODE DETECTOR

The circuit has three parts: 1. the grid circuit indicated by light lines; 2. the filament circuit indicated by heavy lines and 3. the plate circuit indicated by broken lines.

a few of the electrons pass through the grid and reach the plate. The word "few" in the preceding sentence is important. If the grid has sufficient negative charge NONE of the electrons get through the grid to reach the plate. When no electrons pass from the cathode to the plate, no current from the B battery flows in the plate circuit. The electrons are repelled back to the cathode from which they emerged. Since the grid is nearer the cathode than the plate, a positive charge on the grid will have much greater pull on the electrons than an equal positive charge on the plate. Under this condition the combined attraction of the grid and plate causes a large number of electrons to move away from the cathode, pass through the grid and reach the plate. With the passage of a large number of electrons from the cathode to the plate, there is considerable flow of current from the B battery through the plate circuit.

After all this preliminary explanation, we now come to what occurs in a tube when it is used as a detector in a radio receiver. The currents generated in a receiving antenna by incoming signals are alternating currents, that is, alternately positive and negative. If the grid circuit of a triode detector tube is connected to an antenna so that incoming signals are impressed upon it, the charge on the grid will vary in accordance with the signals. So will the number of electrons passing from the cathode to the plate—likewise the volume of current flowing in the plate circuit. The circuits can be so adjusted that even though very feeble signals come from a transmitting station, the variations in current flow in the plate circuit will produce plainly audible sounds in a telephone receiver.

AN EXPLANATION
OF FEEDBACK AND REGENERATION

When Edwin H. Armstrong disclosed his invention called feedback or regeneration, he showed how to make the triode a much better detector than it had ever been before and he also showed for the first time how the tube could be made to oscillate. Until that time a triode was a fairly good detector and an amplifier. But when it was used in the new feedback circuit it became excellent. Radio telegraph signals could be picked up easily for far greater distances than had been possible before.

Feedback takes power or energy from the output or plate circuit of a radio tube and feeds it back into the input or grid circuit and, when it reaches the plate circuit again in amplified form, sends it back again to the grid circuit.

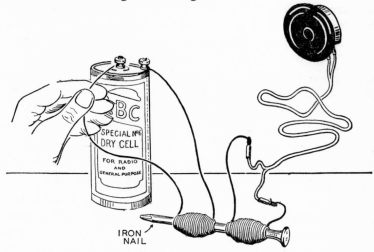

ELECTROMAGNETIC INDUCTION

This experiment demonstrates the principle of electromagnetic induction and shows how energy is transferred from one coil to another by magnetism.

There is more than one way to arrange a feedback circuit. The illustration shows a feedback circuit similar to that used in the regenerative received described later. The feedback is accomplished by means of a coil called a "tickler."

Energy can be transferred from one coil to another by an invisible process called ELECTROMAGNETIC INDUCTION. You can easily find out what electromagnetic induction is by an experiment. Wrap two layers of paper around a large iron nail. Then wind about 40 or 50 turns of insulated wire around the nail near one end. Wind a second similar coil of insulated wire around the nail near the other end. Connect one coil to a telephone receiver and one wire of the other coil to the positive of a dry cell. Listen in the telephone while you tap the unconnected wire of the second coil against the negative terminal of the dry cell. When current from the cell is flowing steadily through the coil, you will not hear anything in the telephone receiver. If you make and break the circuit so as to shut the

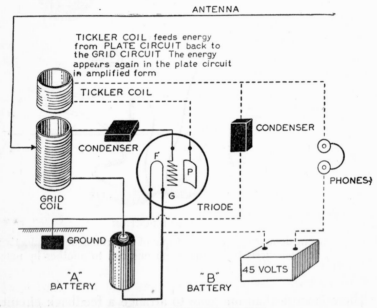

FEEDBACK DETECTOR CIRCUIT

The feedback principle, also called regeneration, feeds energy from the plate or output circuit back into the input or grid circuit. The action is explained at greater length in the text. In the circuit shown above, the transfer of energy from the plate circuit to the grid circuit is accomplished by two coils employing electromagnetic induction. Feedback may also be accomplished by a resistor or a condenser. The light lines indicate the grid circuit; the heavy lines are the filament circuit and the broken lines are the plate circuit.

current on and off, you will hear a clicking sound. The clicks are caused by current INDUCED in the coil connected to the telephone receiver. The current is induced only when the current in the coil connected to the cell is increasing or decreasing.

In the feedback circuit which is illustrated, the tickler coil is connected to the plate circuit and placed near a "grid coil" connected to the grid. The tickler coil transfers energy to the grid coil by electromagnetic induction. In other words, current flowing in the tickler coil induces current in the grid coil. The current induced in the grid coil changes the charge upon the grid of the triode and changes in the charge on the grid produce changes in the current flowing in the plate circuit and tickler coil. If the grid coil is connected so that it receives signals from an antenna, the regenerative or feedback action greatly builds up the signal strength.

If the feedback circuit is adjusted so that the "feed-back" energy travelling from plate circuit to grid circuit and back again is properly timed, the process will repeat itself very rapidly and continue to do so indefinitely. The circuit is then oscillating.

ELECTRON TUBE OSCILLATORS

A very important application of electron tubes is in the generation of alternating voltage and current. When used for this purpose it is called an OSCILLATOR. An oscillator can be adjusted to generate alternating currents of any frequency desired ranging from a few cycles per second to several hundred million. An oscillator does not actually GENERATE current, for example, like an alternator generates current. The tube and its auxiliary circuits CHANGE direct current into alternating current. It converts current fed to it rather than generates.

There are about a dozen kinds of vacuum tube oscillators. One of these is the feedback oscillator—it was the first. There are six well-known varieties of feedback oscillator.

Since the day when Rudolph Hertz first succeeded in pro-

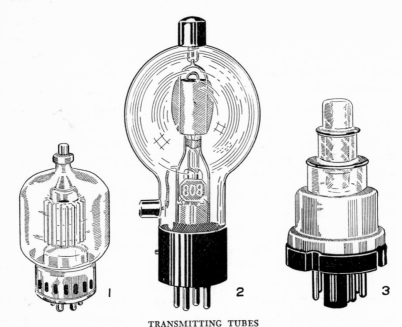

TRANSMITTING TUBES

A transmitter transforms power supplied by AC lines, batteries or generators into radio-frequency power which is made to carry intelligence.
Transmitter tubes may be diodes, triodes, tetrodes or pentodes. Large
transmitter tubes produce large amounts of heat which must be removed
by natural air currents, forced-air cooling, or water cooling. 1. The tube
at the left is a power tetrode with an output of more than 3,000 watts.
2. The tube in the center is a triode. 3. That at the right is a "lighthouse" tube for high frequencies.

ducing electric waves, many methods of generating the high-
frequency currents required in radio have been employed. All
of them have been discarded in favor of the vacuum tube oscillator. It is the most satisfactory—it is portable, has no moving
parts and is comparatively inexpensive.

The power of a single oscillator is quite limited. When more
power is needed the high-frequency currents produced by the
oscillator are sent through amplifier tubes and strengthened
before they reach the antenna.

Electron-tube oscillators have uses other than as sources of high-frequency current for transmitters. They have become an indispensable part of the equipment of scientific, educational and commercial laboratories. The medical treatment called diathermy utilizes an electron tube oscillator. The Cyclotron uses an oscillator. An oscillator is part of every superheterodyne receiver.

All television receivers and the best broadcast receivers employ the circuit invented by Professor Armstrong which he called the superheterodyne. In the superheterodyne, one tube acts as an oscillator. It does not send out radio waves but produces high-frequency currents of a different frequency from the incoming signals. The receiver-produced frequency is mixed with the incoming frequency from the antenna. The result is a new "beat frequency" caused by the interaction of the two frequencies. The "beat frequency" can be amplified more efficiently than the frequencies produced in the antenna by incoming signals and is the reason why a "super" is so sensitive and selective.

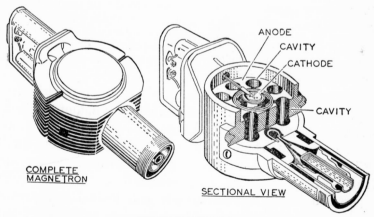

CAVITY MAGNETRON

This is one form of the oscillator used to produce the very high frequencies which generate the microwaves used in radar.

CHAPTER SIX

THINGS YOU SHOULD KNOW ABOUT THE PARTS AND MATERIALS USED TO BUILD RADIO AND ELECTRONIC APPARATUS

An automobile is produced by assembling an engine, carburetor, starter motor, radiator, generator, gears, wheels, axles and other parts in a frame. In much the same way, radio and electronic apparatus is built by assembling various coils, transformers, condensers, sockets, resistors, etc., on a base or chassis.

A few of the parts used in assembling the radio and electronic equipment described in this book have been designed for you to make yourself. Most of the parts you will have to secure ready-made, by purchasing or by salvaging from dismantled radio equipment.

It is not necessary to know a great deal about electricity or radio in order to build radio and electronic equipment. It is only necessary to follow diagrams and instructions carefully. But if you intend to build radio and electronic equipment it will be helpful to learn everything possible about the various resistors, condensers, tubes, etc., used in this work. When you understand the construction of these parts and their purpose, it will be easier to construct and operate your equipment. Last, but not least, this knowledge will make your hobby much more interesting.

This chapter is intended to make you acquainted with the principal parts, materials and tools you will use. All parts, materials and tools are standard and are manufactured in large quantities. They are relatively inexpensive.

Any firm that sells radio equipment or issues a general catalog of radio supplies can supply the parts or materials called for in this book. It is suggested that you send for the catalogs of the mail order radio firms which advertise in radio and popular scientific and mechanical magazines. You can buy anything you may need by mail.

RESISTORS

If you turn a factory-made radio receiver upside down and look at the underside you will see a maze of colored wires and small paper covered cylinders. The small cylinders with three or four colored bands near one end are resistors and they are used to oppose the flow of electricity and reduce the voltage in certain parts of circuits. The resistance of a resistor, or in other words, its ability to oppose an electric current, is measured by a unit called an ohm. Resistors are made in various sizes and in varying resistance ranging from 0.1 to 22,000,000 ohms. Incidentally, 1,000,000 ohms is called a megohm. Radio engineers use the term meg instead of million when speaking of ohms. 22,000,000 ohms is 22 megohms in radio terms. The terminals of the resistors made for radio receivers, amplifiers and other instruments, if they are required to carry only a very small current, have a tinned wire at each end. The body of the resistor is marked with colored bands which indicate its resistance. The colors conform to a standard system adopted by the Radio Manufacturer's Association. Each color represents a number or figure. Some one may give you a few resistors or you may dismantle an old radio to obtain parts and wish to identify the resistors according to their resistance in ohms. Therefore the R.M.A. color code is illustrated here.

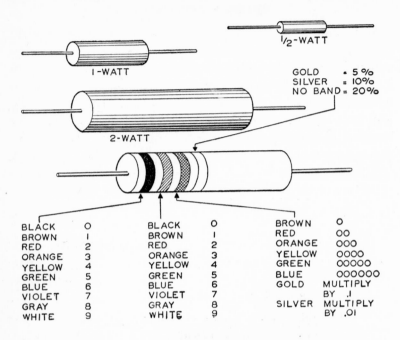

RESISTOR COLOR CODE

The resistance of a resistor is either marked on it with numerals or indicated by color bands. To interpret the color bands hold the resistor so that the end bearing the bands is at your left. Each band is code for a numeral. The end band represents the first figure of the resistance; for example, if it is red, the figure is 2. The second band represents the second figure. If it is green, the second figure is 5. The third band indicates the number of zeros to be placed after the first two figures. If it is green on the resistor we are using as an example place five o's after 25. The resistance is 2,500,000 ohms or 2.5 megohms. If there is no fourth band, the resistance may range 20% either above or below 2,500,000. In other words it may be somewhere between 2,250,000 and 2,750,000. A silver band indicates there may be a 10% variation in resistance. A gold band indicates a 5% variation. Gold-banded resistors are used where accuracy is necessary. They cost more than resistors with a silver fourth band or with no fourth band.

You can identify the capacity of a resistor by its size. A ½-watt resistor will carry only ½ as much energy as a 1-watt resistor and ¼ as much energy as a 2-watt resistor.

VOLUME CONTROLS

Most radio receivers are equipped with a knob to regulate the volume of sound produced by the receiver. The common volume control is a variable or adjustable resistor mounted in a plastic housing with a metal cover. It is equipped with three terminals to which wires can be soldered. The two outside terminals are connected to the ends of the resistor. The center terminal is connected to a movable contact which slides over the resistor when the shaft to which it is attached is turned.

The control can be used to increase or decrease either the resistance or the voltage in a circuit.

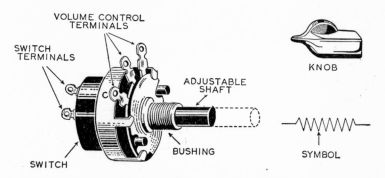

A VOLUME CONTROL AND ITS SYMBOL

Volume controls are resistors whose resistance can be varied by turning a knob. They can be connected so as to control either the current or the voltage in a circuit.

FIXED CONDENSERS

Some of the cylindrical objects on the underside of a radio chassis are fixed condensers. They are an important part of most radio and of some electrical devices in no way related to radio or electronics.

Condenser is the popular name for a device which properly is called a capacitor. A condenser consists of two or more metal surfaces separated and insulated from each other by a layer of insulating material called the *dielectric.*

Condensers store energy and discharge it in the form of electricity. An explanation of how they do this would be rather complicated and perhaps not of great importance to a radio novice. For practical purposes, think of a condenser as a simple and useful device which will store energy for a short time and when included in a circuit will allow an alternating current to pass but completely block a direct current.

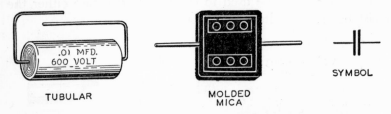

TUBULAR

MOLDED
MICA

SYMBOL

SMALL FIXED CONDENSERS AND THEIR SYMBOL

The "size" of a condenser is not its dimensions in inches or in weight but its CAPACITY to be charged with energy. The unit of capacity is called the *farad,* in honor of the great English scientist, Michael Faraday. Actually, a condenser having a capacity of one FARAD would be so large that its construction is impractical. The common unit for measuring the "electrical size" of a condenser is therefore the MICROFARAD or one-millionth of a farad. Some of the condensers used in radio circuits designed for short waves are so small that their "electrical size" is indicated in MICROMICROFARADS or millionths of a microfarad.

There are two general types of condensers called FIXED and VARIABLE, depending upon whether or not their capacity may be varied. Variable condensers are used principally for tuning.

There is an endless variety of fixed condensers. Catalogs of supply houses dealing in radio parts list dozens of them. Some utilize mica as their dielectric; in others the dielectric is paper.

The cylindrical condensers which are enclosed in a cardboard tube usually consist of thin sheets of metal foil separated by paper dielectric. There is a flexible wire attached to each end of the tube and these are the condenser terminals. The capacity of this type of condenser is always marked on the cardboard case.

Condensers enclosed in a flat, rectangular Bakelite case consist usually of thin sheets of metal foil separated by a mica dielectric. This type may have wire terminals, screw terminals or metal ears to which wires can be soldered. The capacity of a mica condenser is marked upon it in figures or indicated by colored dots in accordance with the R.M.A. color code for mica fixed condensers.

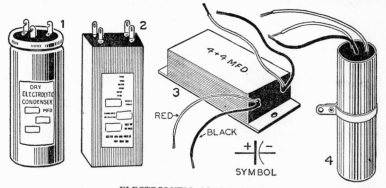

ELECTROLYTIC CONDENSERS

These fixed condensers of large capacity are used in radio receivers operated on 120-volt current. The terminals of an electrolytic condenser are usually marked + or — to indicate the positive and negative terminals. The capacity is marked on the condenser case. Some electrolytic condensers are enclosed in a metal case (1). Others have cardboard or paper cases (2, 3, 4).

VARIABLE CONDENSERS

Variable condensers are used for tuning radio circuits. The name "variable condenser" belongs to a type of condenser whose capacity may be changed by turning a knob. The common form of variable condenser consists of several movable semicircular (half circles) aluminum plates mounted on a shaft and a group of fixed or non-moving aluminum plates. Sometimes the plates are made of brass. The group of movable plates is called the rotor and the group of fixed plates is called the stator. When the knob is turned the rotor plates move in or out of the spaces between the stator plates. The stator and rotor are insulated from each other and when the rotor plates are moved in between the stator plates they do not come into electrical contact. There is a small air space between them. This air is the dielectric.

A variable condenser is adjusted to its maximum capacity when the rotor plates are completely between the stator plates.

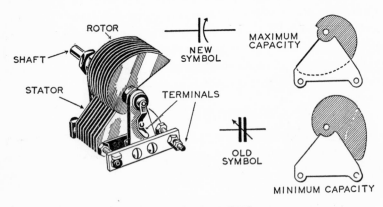

VARIABLE CONDENSERS

Variable condensers are used for tuning circuits and consist of a number of movable, semi-circular, metal plates which rotate between fixed plates. A variable condenser should be handled with care to avoid bending the movable plates and thus cause them to touch the fixed plates. The curved arrow in the symbol representing a variable condenser represents the movable plates. It is important to connect the movable plates and the fixed plates exactly as indicated in wiring diagrams. In the diagrams at the right, the shaded plate is the movable one. A condenser is at its maximum capacity when the movable plates are interleaved with the fixed plates as far as possible.

When the rotor is turned so that its plates are no longer between the stator plates, the capacity of the condenser is at a minimum.

Some of the radio receivers described in this book employ variable condensers for tuning.

Variable condensers may differ slightly in some of the details of their construction but they all employ the same principles. It is customary to build variable condensers so that the rotor and the frame of the condenser are electrically connected and the stator is insulated from the frame. When a variable condenser is part of a radio instrument which has a metal chassis, the rotor and the frame are always connected or "grounded" to the chassis. This is done to eliminate "body effect" or changes in tuning which might be caused by moving the fingers to or from the tuning knob. In circuit diagrams using symbols (schematic) a straight line indicates the stator of a variable condenser and a curved arrow indicates the rotor. It is important to connect a variable condenser exactly as shown in such diagrams and not connect a wire to the stator which should go to the rotor and vice versa. Otherwise, body effect may make it difficult to tune the apparatus accurately.

TELEPHONE RECEIVERS

A telephone receiver changes the energy of electric currents into sounds. It is one of the most sensitive of electrical instruments. Amazingly small electric currents will produce sounds in a telephone receiver.

You can use a common telephone receiver in your radio experiments, but receivers made especially for radio do not cost much and give much better results. Two receivers are better than one for listening to weak signals. A receiver for each ear will shut out unwanted sounds.

Telephone receivers for radio use are the small, light-weight type commonly called "watch-case" or "head-phones." Amateur radio operators refer to them as "cans." A complete radio head-set consists of two watch-case receivers with an adjustable headband which holds the receivers close to the ears. The receivers are connected in series and provided with a long flexible connecting wire called a telephone "cord."

A telephone receiver consists of one or two electromagnets, a permanent magnet and a disk of thin sheet iron known as the diaphragm. The electromagnets are mounted on the permanent magnet and set under the center of the diaphragm. The space between

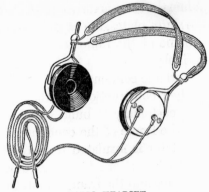

RADIO HEADSET

A complete radio headset consists of a pair of receivers fitted with a headband so that a receiver is closely held to each ear. The receivers are connected in series with each other by a flexible wire called a telephone "cord."

the diaphragm and the electromagnets is only a few thousandths of an inch. This close adjustment must be maintained if the receiver is to keep its sensitivity. Take good care of a radio headset. Do not drop it. Keep the caps screwed tightly on the cases. Do not unscrew the cap of a sensitive telephone receiver to see what is inside. You may unintentionally bend the diaphragm. If the diaphragm is not perfectly flat, the receiver will not be sensitive.

Telephone receivers for radio use are wound with wire of much smaller diameter than those made for a telephone. The finer wire makes it possible to wind a greater number of turns of wire on the electromagnets. This makes radio headphones more sensitive to weak currents than the common receiver for telephone use. Wire of small diameter has more resistance than larger wire. The common telephone receiver has a resistance of about 75 ohms. The phones in a radio headset of good quality have a resistance of 2000 to 3000 ohms per pair and are so sensitive that sounds are produced in them by the tiny electric current generated when the cord tips are rubbed together while held against the tongue.

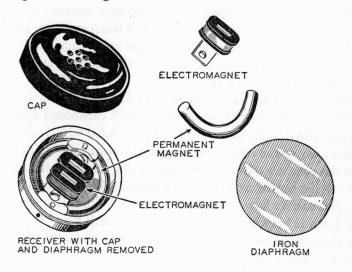

ELECTROMAGNET

CAP

PERMANENT MAGNET

ELECTROMAGNET

RECEIVER WITH CAP
AND DIAPHRAGM REMOVED

IRON
DIAPHRAGM

INSIDE A TELEPHONE RECEIVER

This is the type of telephone receiver used in radio. An amazingly small amount of electrical energy flowing through its electromagnets will produce sounds audible to human ears. A receiver consists of a case, cap, a pair of small electromagnets, a permanent magnet and a thin sheet iron diaphragm.

SPEAKERS

Only one person at a time can listen to a telephone receiver but a speaker will produce sounds with enough volume to be heard by a group of people.

A speaker (also called a loudspeaker) is like a telephone receiver in that it changes the energy of electric currents into sound waves. It is not as sensitive as a telephone receiver and in order to operate requires stronger currents. But it produces louder sounds. The weak currents direct from a detector are seldom strong enough to operate a speaker. Detector currents must be strengthened by passing through an audio amplifier before they will produce sounds of any appreciable volume from a speaker.

Speakers can be divided into two groups, namely: dynamic speakers and permanent speakers. Most small speakers used in table model and portable radio receivers are permanent magnet speakers (called PM speakers by radio technicians) and are the type we are interested in.

Sound waves are produced in a speaker by the vibrations of a cone-shaped paper diaphragm. A small cardboard cylinder, wound with a single layer of very fine insulated wire, is attached to the apex of the cone. This winding, known as a "voice coil," and the cone are mounted on a metal ring and adjusted so that the coil lies between the poles of a magnet. When currents from a radio receiver flow through the voice coil, the coil moves back and forth in step with changes in the current. Since the coil is attached to the paper cone, the cone moves also, and when the cone moves it produces sound waves.

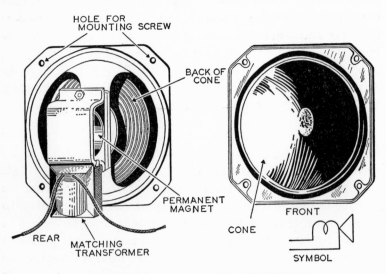

SMALL PERMANENT MAGNET SPEAKER

The voice coil of a speaker cannot be connected directly to an amplifier and give satisfactory results. The voice coil should be connected to the secondary of a "matching" transformer. The primary of the transformer is connected to the amplifier.

Speakers are rated according to the diameter of their paper cone. A 6-inch speaker has a 6-inch cone; a 5-inch speaker has a 5-inch cone, etc.

HOOK-UP WIRE

What sort of wire should be used for wiring or hooking up the parts of apparatus described later? The answer is: almost any type of insulated copper wire provided it is not smaller than No. 20 or larger than No. 16 B. & S. gauge. Tinned wire is most desirable because solder will adhere to it more readily than to bare copper. A novice may experience difficulty in cutting the insulation from the ends of some varieties of wire. It is not always easy to do this without nicking the wire. Wire will break easily at any point where it is nicked, so be careful.

Two varieties of small wire made especially for hook-up purposes are "thermoplastic hook-up" wire and "push-back hook-up" wire. Both are tinned. The insulation strips off easily from the thermoplastic wire. It is not necessary to strip the insulation off the ends of push-back wire. Merely cut a piece of wire to the desired length, push the insulation back from the end while soldering and then slide it back in place. You can buy hook-up wire from any radio dealer.

CHAPTER SEVEN

CRYSTAL DETECTORS

You would hardly expect to find a good radio detector by digging into the earth for it. Nevertheless, for about ten years prior to the entry of the U. S. A. into World War I the best detectors for wireless telegraph signals came out of the earth. They were small pieces of such minerals as galena, iron pyrites, zincite and others.

The use of crystals as detectors in wireless telegraphy began in 1906 when Gen. H. H. Dunwoody of the U. S. Army discovered that a small piece of Carborundum would act as a detector of Hertzian waves. Carborundum is an abrasive which is made at Niagara Falls by heating coke, sand, sawdust and salt in an electric furnace.

For the information of those who may wish to experiment with Carborundum, the best Carborundum detector crystals are usually bluish-gray. Place the crystal in some sort of metal clamping device and bring a pointed copper wire to bear firmly against a sensitive spot.

General Dunwoody's discovery prompted another American inventor, Greenleaf W. Pickard, to search the mineral world for detector material and he patented the use of silicon, zincite, chalcopyrites, bornite and molybdenite as detectors. The Dunwoody and Pickard patents have long since expired.

Mineral, or "crystal" detectors, as they are popularly called, are obsolete in radio broadcasting and in radio communications, having been superseded by the far more stable and sensitive electron tube. However, they are still of interest to the young

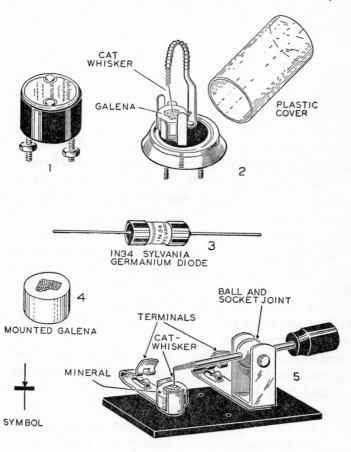

CAT WHISKER

GALENA

PLASTIC COVER

1

2

IN34 SYLVANIA GERMANIUM DIODE

3

4

MOUNTED GALENA

BALL AND SOCKET JOINT

TERMINALS

CAT-WHISKER

MINERAL

5

SYMBOL

CRYSTAL DETECTORS WHICH YOU CAN BUY

1. Fixed crystal detector which stays in adjustment but is not always so sensitive as the adjustable type. 2. Enclosed adjustable detector. The transparent plastic cover protects the crystal from dirt. 3. Germanium diode. 4. Galena crystal mounted in low-temperature alloy. 5. Low-priced crystal detector stand.

experimenter—a crystal is the simplest form of detector and provides an inexpensive and easy way to become acquainted with radio.

There are a number of substances which can be used as crystal detectors. Some are natural minerals, others are products of the electric furnace and chemical laboratory.

Galena, a silvery appearing natural mineral composed of lead in combination with sulfur, is the most sensitive crystal detector. Not every piece of galena will prove to be a good radio detector. Furthermore, the whole surface of every piece is not sensitive. There are small areas which are sensitive and they can be located by placing the mineral in a radio receiver and at the same time exploring the surface. Point the end of a white chalk crayon and when a sensitive spot is found, mark it with the point of the chalk. Then split off most of the dead area with a knife so that the sensitive spot will not be difficult to locate again. Chalk is used for the purpose because it will not destroy the sensitivity of the crystal and is easily seen.

The most sensitive form of galena contains a small percentage of silver and is called argentiferous galena. Its surface is more granular than common galena. Argentiferous galena is sometimes sold to amateurs under the name "steel" galena.

Galena and some other minerals perform best as detectors when they are embedded (with the sensitive area exposed) in a small slug of alloy having a low melting temperature. The alloys used for this purpose (Wood's metal is one and it can be purchased from dealers in chemical supplies) melt in boiling water and even at lower temperatures. They are used because when some galena specimens are subjected to higher temperatures than the temperature of boiling water their value as a radio detector is destroyed.

Tested and mounted galena crystals can be purchased from radio dealers. The price is usually less than 25 cents.

Detector Stands. When a piece of mineral is used as a radio detector it is usually clamped in a detector "stand." The stand has an adjustable contact point which can be made to touch any part of the upper surface of the mineral. Detector stands can be homemade. On the other hand, the factory-made variety can be purchased at a cost of a few cents and usually has some advantages.

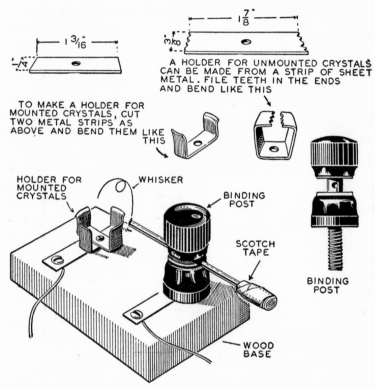

A CRYSTAL DETECTOR STAND WHICH YOU CAN MAKE

Detector stands intended for galena crystals are provided with a fine wire spring called a "cat-whisker." The point of the whisker is brought into contact with a sensitive spot in the galena and the pressure adjusted until the signals in the headphones are loudest. The whisker on a homemade detector stand should be a piece of No. 30 B. & S. gauge spring phosphor bronze, brass or German silver wire. Copper does not have enough spring to make a satisfactory whisker.

A receiver with a crystal detector will enable you to experiment and discover some of the minerals which will receive radio signals. If you have a mineral collection, check it to see if it contains any specimens of the minerals listed below. All of these minerals are detectors.

COMMON NAME	CHEMICAL NAME
Anatase	Titanium dioxide
Bornite	Copper-iron sulfide
Cerusite	Lead carbonate
Chalcocite	Copper sulfide
Chalcopyrites	Copper-iron sulfide
Copper Pyrites	Copper sulfide
Domeykite	Copper arsenide
Galena	Lead sulfide
Hecsite	Telluride of silver and gold
Iron Pyrites (Fools' Gold)	Iron sulfide
Molybdenite	Molybdenum sulfide
Niccolite	Nickel arsenide
Octahedrite	Titanium oxide
Psilomelane	Manganese manganite
Stibnite	Antimony sulfide
Zincite	Zinc oxide
Zirconium	Zirconium

Silicon.   Next to oxygen, silicon is the most abundant element. The white or colorless, extremely hard constituent of quartz and sand is *silica*, a combination of silicon with oxygen. No one probably ever saw pure silicon until the illustrious Swedish chemist, Jons Jacob Berzelius, produced some in the form of a brown powder more than 125 years ago. Silicon can take three forms: a dull-brown amorphous powder, shining metallic scales resembling graphite and a steel-gray crystalline mass. The crystalline form of silicon is prepared at Niagara

Falls by heating silica with carbon in an electric furnace. It is used to alloy with iron to make special steels.

The steel-gray crystalline form of silicon makes an excellent radio detector. It will not respond to far-away stations as well as galena but it will produce louder signals from near-by stations. The whisker used to make contact with a sensitive spot on a piece of galena should be stiffer and bear against the spot more firmly than the whisker used with galena.

Iron Pyrites. The cubical crystals of this mineral are heavy and of a brass-yellow color. A popular name for this combination of iron and sulfur is "fools' gold." Many uninformed explorers and prospectors have brought in a heavy load of iron pyrites with the mistaken belief they had discovered gold.

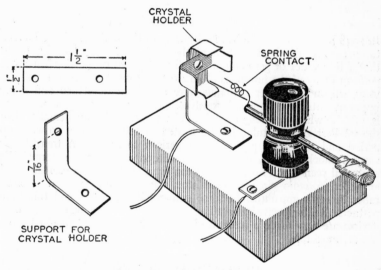

CRYSTAL HOLDER

SPRING CONTACT

$1\frac{1}{2}"$

SUPPORT FOR CRYSTAL HOLDER

HOMEMADE DETECTOR USING SILICON
OR IRON PYRITES

The spring contact should push against silicon and iron pyrites with greater pressure than is used with galena. Notice the difference in the shape of the spring contact in the illustration above and the shape of the whisker in the preceding illustration. They are designed so that the spring contact will have more pressure than the whisker.

A pointed gold wire makes the best contact with the sensitive spots on a piece of iron pyrites used as a radio detector. For experimental purposes the point of a gold stickpin is a good substitute for gold wire.

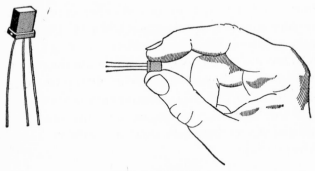

THE TRANSISTOR

In 1948 John Bardeen and W. H. Brattain of the Bell Telephone Laboratories announced the invention of the transistor. They had discovered that a tiny wafer of germanium crystal with three connecting wires can perform many of the functions of an electron tube. Since then transistors using silicon and other materials have also been developed and many improvements in design and construction accomplished. The transistor is a device which was long needed in electronics. It is much smaller than the smallest vacuum tube, has no heated cathode, requires no warm-up period and very little power in comparison to a tube. A transistor is rugged, shock-resistant, unaffected by dampness and has a normal life of several years if not mistreated. It can serve as a detector, oscillator and amplifier in radio circuits. Transistors have entirely replaced electron tubes in some apparatus. In some equipment transistors and tubes are partners. Radio receivers, amplifiers, hearing aids and many electronic devices are now made a fraction of their former size and weight by the use of transistors.

GERMANIUM DIODES

The most satisfactory crystal detector is a small cylindrical shaped device called a germanium diode. It consists of a tiny speck of germanium crystal enclosed in a small tube. Germanium is one of the elements—a scarce grayish-colored metal which was discovered by Clemens Winkler. Winkler was a German chemist and he named his find Germanium in honor of his fatherland.

A germanium diode costs about one dollar. If you can afford one, it will prove to be far more satisfactory than any other crystal detector you can build or buy. It is sensitive, needs no adjustment and does not get out of order unless mistreated. Never solder any wires or other connections to the terminals of a germanium diode. The heat of soldering may spoil it. Also, do not use it for any experiments whereby more than a few thousandths of an ampere pass through, or it may be burned out.

Silicon diodes in which the germanium is replaced by a small piece of the element, silicon, are also manufactured. Germanium and silicon diodes are used in television receivers and in microwave radio.

CHAPTER EIGHT

SIMPLE, PRACTICAL RADIO RECEIVERS AND HOW TO BUILD THEM

Tuning. An agreement among the nations of the world requires all radio transmitters to be licensed. Under this agreement a transmitter is licensed for operation only on the frequency (or frequencies) assigned to it. Consequently, it is necessary to adjust or TUNE a transmitter so that it will produce waves only of the frequency or frequencies assigned to the station. Radio receivers must be adjusted or tuned to bring in signals properly. Tuning a receiver strengthens the desired signals and bars out signals from other stations which are unwanted at the time.

A crystal detector and a telephone receiver connected to an antenna and to the ground in the manner illustrated in the diagram on this page will receive radio signals. A simple, untuned receiver such as this has a great drawback. It will receive the signals of more than one station at the same time and will not receive signals from distant stations. It is an *untuned* radio receiver. A tuned receiver does not have these disadvantages.

The simplest tuning device is a tuning coil. It is not the best or the most efficient tuning apparatus but it is easy to make. For that reason the first two radio receivers described in this book employ tuning coils.

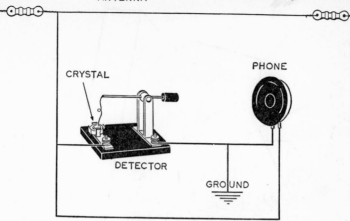

ANTENNA

CRYSTAL

PHONE

DETECTOR

GROUND

AN UNTUNED RADIO RECEIVER

This simple receiver will bring in radio signals but its limited range and lack of tuning make it impractical. It will bring in signals from several stations at the same time.

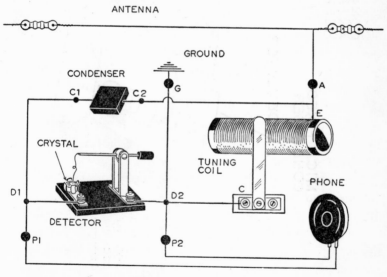

ANTENNA

GROUND

CONDENSER

C1   C2   G   A

                                                     E

CRYSTAL

                                        TUNING
                                        COIL

                                                     PHONE

D1   D2   C

DETECTOR

P1   P2

CIRCUIT DIAGRAM OF A
SIMPLE TUNED RADIO RECEIVER

Some sort of tuning device is necessary to select desired signals and shut out unwanted ones. A tuning coil is the simplest form of tuner but not the most efficient one.

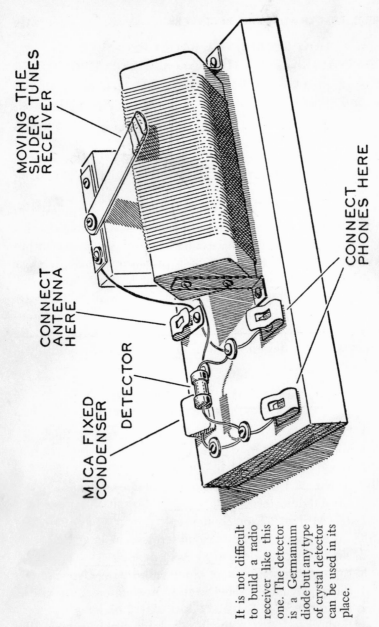

MOVING THE
SLIDER TUNES
RECEIVER

CONNECT
ANTENNA
HERE

MICA FIXED
CONDENSER

DETECTOR

CONNECT
PHONES HERE

HOMEMADE RADIO RECEIVER

WITH CRYSTAL DETECTOR AND SINGLE-SLIDER TUNING COIL

It is not difficult to build a radio receiver like this one. The detector is a Germanium diode but any type of crystal detector can be used in its place.

HOW TO BUILD A RADIO RECEIVER
WITH CRYSTAL DETECTOR AND SINGLE-SLIDER TUNER

The simplest practical radio receiver which is worth the time and effort to build consists of a single-slider tuning coil, a crystal detector, a fixed condenser and a telephone receiver. Such a radio receiver costs little and does not require much time to build. If you have never built radio apparatus, the experience gained in building this receiver will be valuable in making more elaborate instruments.

If there is a radio broadcasting station within 50 miles, you can listen to its programs with this receiver. The sounds produced in the headphones will not be loud unless you are within a few miles of the station—but they will have amazingly clear and natural tones.

Before starting the construction work, obtain all of the materials in the following list. Consult the index for the page numbers where mica condensers, crystal detectors, headphones and magnet wires are described. Read about these parts before you purchase them.

MATERIALS REQUIRED FOR
CONSTRUCTING THE RECEIVER

  1 Wood base 7⅝ in. x 5 in. and from ½ in. to ¾ in. thick
  1 Wood block 2½ in. x 2⅛ in. x ¾ in.
  1 Wood core 4 in. x 1½ in. x 1½ in.
130 ft. No. 26 B.S. gauge enameled magnet wire
  1 Crystal detector
  1 .004 Mfd mica fixed condenser
 18 No. 5 round head brass wood screws ½ in. long
  2 No. 5 round head wood screws 1 in. long
  8 Brass or copper washers which will slip over No. 5 screws
  1 Piece galvanized sheet iron approximately 2 in. x 4 in.
  1 Piece No. 14 B. S. bare copper wire 2 in. long
  1 Radio headset or a single telephone receiver wound for radio use

Liquid shellac or varnish and brush
4 Binding posts or Fahnestock connectors

In addition to the materials listed above, materials to build the coil winder described later in this chapter may be required.

The Base.   Start by making the base. This can be made of any variety of soft wood (except balsa) from ½ in. to ¾ in. in thickness provided it is seasoned and thoroughly dry. The end of a wooden packing box is suitable lumber if it is thick enough. Smooth rough spots by sandpapering and then give the whole base—top, bottom and edges—a coat of shellac. Shellac dries quickly. Apply a second coat when the first has dried. The shellac will improve the appearance of the base but its main purpose is to keep moisture out of the wood. Moisture in materials used in the construction of radio apparatus may weaken signals. The shellac also will help prevent the base from warping. The wood must be thoroughly dry before the shellac is applied.

Caution: Do not use paint or enamel on the wooden parts of radio apparatus. These finishes usually contain metallic substances which may cause current leaks and even short circuits.

The wood block which supports one end of the slider should be shellacked before it is fastened to the base.

The Tuning Coil.   The core of the tuning coil is made of pine or other soft wood and it also must be thoroughly dry. The core is 4 in. long and 1½ in. x 1½ in. in section. (If a piece of soft pine (not yellow pine) which is 1½ in. thick cannot be obtained, glue together two strips 4 in. x 1½ x ¾ in. or three strips 4 in. x 1½ in. x ½ in.) The edges are rounded slightly by sandpapering. Drill a small hole ½ in. from each end so that the ends of a wire can be anchored by looping through the holes. The holes should be near a corner.

If the core is to be wound in the homemade winding machine bore a ½ in. diameter hole in each end exactly along the axis of the core and one inch deep. You can find the exact spot to place the center of the auger bit by drawing two diagonal lines on each end of the core. The point at which the lines cross is the place to start the drill.

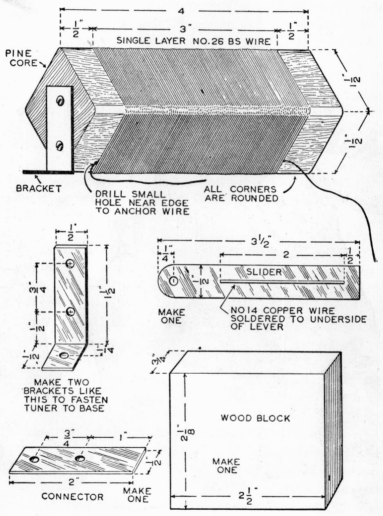

PARTS FOR THE SINGLE-SLIDER TUNER

These parts are homemade. Their construction is explained in the text.

WALT
REED

The coil consists of a single layer of No. 26 B. & S. enamel wire wound smoothly and tightly on the wooden core. The winding starts and ends ½ inch from the end of the core and is given a coat of shellac when completed. The shellac helps prevent the wire from becoming loose if the core shrinks slightly. Before winding, the core should be dried for a few hours by placing it on a warm radiator or in a warm oven (not hot). If dried in an oven, the oven door should remain open. After the core has been dried and while it is still warm, it should be shellacked or varnished to prevent the wood from absorbing moisture again.

The wire must be wound in a smooth, even layer. It is difficult to wind a tuning coil without some sort of winding device. Perhaps some one with a lathe-equipped home workshop will wind a coil for you. Or perhaps you can do this yourself on a lathe in the shop at your school.

If a metal turning lathe is used, one end of the wood core is placed in a chuck on the headstock of the lathe. The other end is supported on the center in the tailstock. The lathe should be turned slowly by hand by pulling on the belt. If a wood-turning lathe is used the wooden core for the tuner is mounted between centers as if it were to be turned. Remember to turn the lathe by hand. If you have not had experience winding coils, you will not have much luck winding the coil with power.

Those who are not fortunate enough to have a lathe available should build a winding machine. This will not require much time.

The Slider and Other Metal Parts. The slider, the two brackets which support the tuning coil and the small strip labeled "connector" in one of the drawings are made of galvanized iron sheet. This is slightly thicker and stiffer than the metal used in cans but you will not find it difficult to cut with a small pair of tinner's snips. You can obtain galvanized iron sheet at a tinsmith's or sheet metal working shop. It is inexpensive—a piece 2 in. by 4 in. is all that is required. You may be able to obtain a piece of scrap at no cost.

Cut the metal into strips ½ in. wide. Three strips ½ in. wide and 2 in. long and one strip ½ in. wide and 3½ in. long are required. Drill and bend two of the strips to form the "L"-shaped brackets which support the tuning coil (see illustrations). Drill the third 2-in. strip to make the connector. Mark the location of the holes with a center punch and make the holes with a No. 29 or No. 30 twist drill. If the metal strips have sharp corners and edges, dull them with a file. The 3½ in. strip is used to make the slider. One end of the slider is pivoted so that the other end can be moved to the left or right. A short piece (2 in. long) of No. 14 B. S. solid copper wire 2 in. long is soldered to the underside. This is the wire size commonly used for house wiring. You can get a scrap piece at any electrical shop. This wire makes contact with the wire on the tuning coil when the slider is moved to tune in a station. The wire makes contact with only one or two turns at a time. A flat strip of metal sliding over the edge of the tuning coil would make contact with several turns at a time and weaken signals.

The Condenser. The small fixed condenser should be a mica condenser, preferably one having a capacity of .004 mfd. Any small condenser of approximately this capacity, even a paper condenser of .01 mfd capacity will give fair results, but the type and size first mentioned will be most satisfactory.

The Detector. The illustrations show the receiver to be equipped with a germanium diode detector. This detector is most satisfactory because it is sensitive and requires no adjustment but any type of crystal detector can be used. If a germanium diode is too expensive, use any of the other detectors described in the preceding chapter.

Terminals or Binding Posts. The illustrations show Fahnestock connectors. Use any type of binding post. Four are required.

Assembling and Wiring the Receiver. The wood block

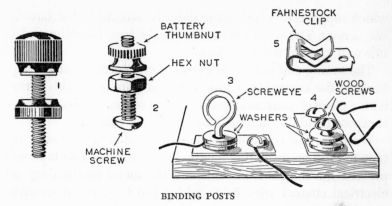

BINDING POSTS

1 and 5 are inexpensive factory-made binding posts for fastening wires. 2, 3, and 4 show how you can make your own binding posts.

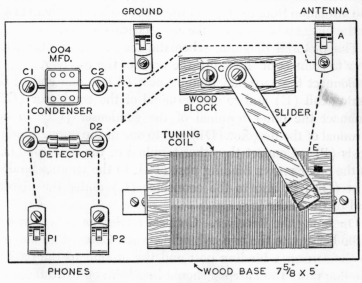

PLAN OF THE RECEIVER
WITH SINGLE-SLIDER TUNER

The dotted lines indicate the connecting wires. The terminals and binding posts are lettered so that they can be identified with the corresponding binding posts and terminals in the schematic and pictorial circuit diagrams.

which supports one end of the slider is fastened to the base by two screws. The screws pass through the base from the underside and upward into the block.

The tuning coil is mounted so that one corner is at the top. Remove the enamel insulation from the wire along this corner with a piece of fine sandpaper (No. 00) so that the bare copper is exposed and the slider can make contact with it.

Wrap the free end of the slider with Scotch tape or adhesive tape to form an insulating handle for the fingers. The tape will prevent the fingers from touching the metal and making an electrical contact with it. Touching the bare metal weakens signals.

The wires which connect the binding posts, tuning coil, detector and condenser run over the top of the base. Remove the insulation from the ends of the wires and scrape them bright at the places where they make an electrical contact.

The pictorial diagram, schematic diagram and plan show how to connect or "hook up" the parts of the receiver.

Connect the ANTENNA binding post (A) to one end of the tuning coil (E) and to one terminal of the condenser (C2). Connect the other terminal of the condenser (C1) to one terminal of the detector (D1) and to one of the PHONE binding posts (P1). Connect the other terminal of the detector (D2) to the other PHONE binding post (P2), to the GROUND binding post (G) and also to the connector (C) under the pivoted end of the slider.

Operating the Receiver.   Connect a telephone receiver or a radio headset to the PHONE binding posts. Connect an antenna to the ANTENNA binding post and the ground to the GROUND binding post. The antenna should be a wire 50 to 75 feet long and be insulated from its supports. The ground should be a wire connected to a water, gas or steam pipe. Antennas and ground connections are described in more detail in the chapter called "Antennas and Ground Connections."

After connecting the receiver to the aerial and ground, test the detector to insure that it is in proper adjustment. If the detector is a germanium diode, there is no need to test or adjust it. If the detector has an adjustable contact or whisker, it should be tested so as to insure that the whisker or contact wire rests on a sensitive spot on the crystal. To do this, a small

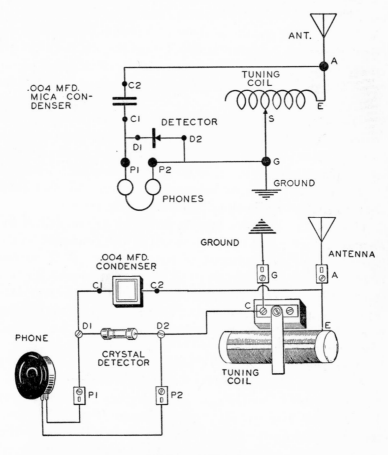

CIRCUIT DIAGRAMS

The top diagram is schematic. The lower diagram is pictorial. These diagrams and the plan show how to hook-up the single slider-tuner receiver.

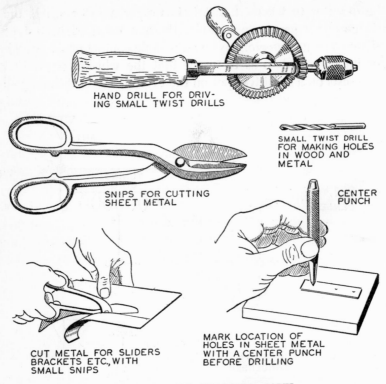

HAND DRILL FOR DRIV-
ING SMALL TWIST DRILLS

SMALL TWIST DRILL
FOR MAKING HOLES
IN WOOD AND
METAL

SNIPS FOR CUTTING
SHEET METAL

CENTER
PUNCH

CUT METAL FOR SLIDERS
BRACKETS ETC., WITH
SMALL SNIPS

MARK LOCATION OF
HOLES IN SHEET METAL
WITH A CENTER PUNCH
BEFORE DRILLING

TOOLS FOR MAKING THE METAL PARTS
OF THE RADIO RECEIVERS

buzzer, a dry cell, and a switch are required. The use of a test buzzer is explained at the end of this chapter.

When the sensitive spot on the crystal (where the sound of the buzzer is heard loudest) has been found, the receiver is in condition to bring in signals. Move the slider to the left or right until the signals from the station you have selected to listen to are loudest. When this place on the tuning coil has been found the No. 14 wire soldered to the bottom of the slider should rest on a single turn of wire on the coil and not touch two turns so that a short circuit is formed between them.

Do not expect to hear many stations with this receiver and do not be surprised if you hear more than one at the same time. If the receiver is equipped with a detector having a whisker or wire contact, be careful not to jar it. It is easily knocked out of adjustment. When this happens, use the test buzzer to readjust the detector, or search the surface of the crystal, using the signals from a broadcasting station to indicate when a sensitive spot has been found.

A single-slider tuning coil is not as efficient as a double-slider tuning coil or as a coupler. You can improve the operation of the receiver—it will be more selective, that is tune better and bring in more stations—if you build a wave trap and connect it as explained later in this chapter. A loading coil connected to the receiver will increase its frequency range and consequently may increase the number of stations you can tune in.

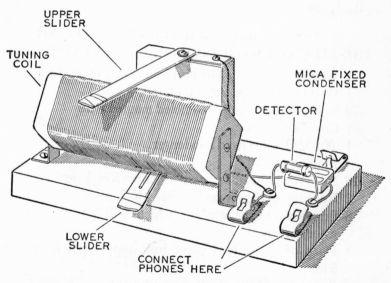

UPPER SLIDER

TUNING COIL

MICA FIXED CONDENSER

DETECTOR

LOWER SLIDER

CONNECT PHONES HERE

HOMEMADE RADIO RECEIVER
WITH DOUBLE-SLIDER TUNING COIL

HOW TO BUILD A RADIO RECEIVER WITH CRYSTAL DETECTOR AND DOUBLE-SLIDER TUNING COIL

A double-slider tuner will tune more efficiently than a single-slider coil. It is more selective—it will tune out unwanted stations better. You can change the receiver with a single-slider tuner into one with a double-slider. Or you can "start from scratch" and build the more selective receiver without first building the simpler one.

To change the single-slider coil to one with a double-slider, it is necessary to make two new sliders, an additional connecting strip and a new wood block. The sliders and wood block are different in size from those which were previously described and illustrated. It will be necessary also to rewire the receiver because a different hookup is used.

If you plan to build the receiver with double-slider tuner, first read the instructions for making the single-slider receiver. The parts are alike or nearly alike and the same construction methods are used.

MATERIALS REQUIRED FOR CONSTRUCTING THE RECEIVER WITH DOUBLE-SLIDER TUNING COIL

    1 Wood base 7⅞ in. x 5 in. and from ½ in. to ¾ in. thick
    1 Wood block 2½ in. x 2⅜ in. x ¾ in.
175 ft. No. 26 B.S. gauge enameled magnet wire
    1 Crystal detector
    1 .004 Mfd. mica fixed condenser
    4 Binding posts
  16 No. 5 round head brass wood screws ½ in. long
    2 No. 5 round head wood screws 1 in. long
    8 Brass or copper washers which will slip over No. 5 wood screws
    1 Piece of galvanized sheet iron approximately 3 in. x 5 in.
    2 Pieces No. 14 B.S. gauge bare copper wire 3 in. long
    4 Binding posts or Fahnestock connectors

1 Radio headset or a single telephone receiver wound for
radio use

1 Telephone cord for radio receiver

The wood base, detector, condenser, binding posts, connecting strip and brackets which hold the tuning coil are the same
as those described for the receiver with a single-slider tuner.

The wood block is 2½ in. x 2⅜ in. x ¾ in. Notice that it is ¼ in.
higher than the one used on the single-slider receiver.

Dry the base, wood block and tuning coil core and give
them a coat of shellac on all surfaces.

The pine core for the tuning coil is 4¾ in. long and 1½ in. x
1½ in. in section. Wind it with a single layer of No. 26 B.S.
enameled magnet wire. Start and finish the winding ⅜ in. from

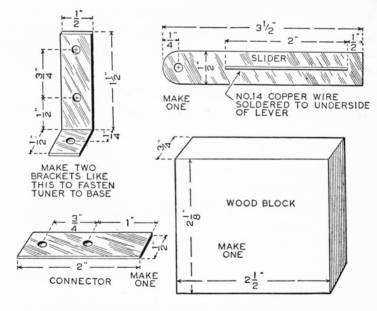

PARTS FOR THE DOUBLE-SLIDER TUNING COIL

Except for dimensions, these parts are the same as those used for the
single-slider tuner.

the ends of the core. Give the winding a coat of shellac when finished.

The brackets should be fastened to the ends of the core so that when the coil is mounted on the base the lower corner is ¼ in. above the surface of the base. This space is necessary to provide room for the lower slider. One slider makes contact with the bottom of the coil; the other makes contact with the top. Remove the enamel insulation from the wire along both the top and bottom corners of the coil by rubbing with No. 00 sandpaper so that the sliders can make a good electrical contact with the wire.

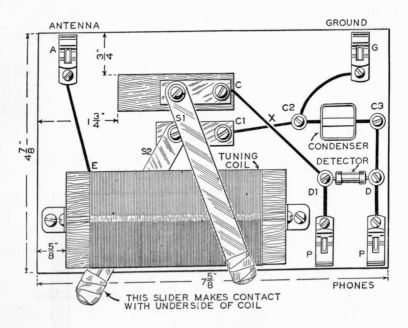

PLAN OF THE RECEIVER
WITH DOUBLE-SLIDER TUNER

The two wires which cross at the point marked "X" in the illustration are not electrically connected and should be insulated from one another. Consult the plan and the schematic diagram when hooking up the receiver.

The two sliders are alike. Make each from a strip of galvanized iron sheet ½ in. wide and 4¾ in. long. Solder a straight
piece of No. 14 B. S. solid copper wire 3 in. long to each slider
as shown in the illustration. The wire stiffens the slider and is
the part which makes contact with the wire on the tuning coil
when the slider is moved to tune in a station.

The lower slider (marked S2 in plan) is pivoted on a round
head screw in the base. The side on which the No. 14 wire is
soldered is turned upward. The upper slider (S1) is pivoted on
a round head screw in the center of the wood block. This slider
(S1) is turned so that the No. 14 wire is on the underside. A
metal connecting strip (C) is placed under each slider between
the slider and the base. Use a washer under the head of both
screws. It may be necessary to bend both sliders slightly so
that they bear against the tuning coil with sufficient pressure
to make good electrical contact.

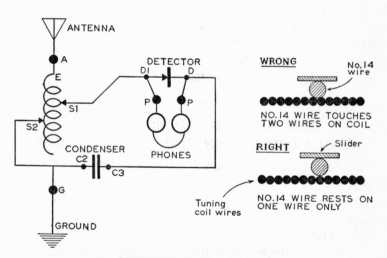

SCHEMATIC CIRCUIT DIAGRAM
OF RECEIVER WITH DOUBLE-SLIDER TUNER

Signals will be louder when the slider rests on a single turn of wire than
when it rests on two. See right-hand sketch.

Assembling and Connecting. The sketch of the finished receiver and the plan show better than words can how the various parts are assembled on the wood base. The plan and the circuit diagram show how the parts are connected. It is essential to remove the insulation from the ends of all connecting wires for a distance of ½ inch and to scrape the exposed copper bright and clean.

Connect the ANTENNA binding post (A) to one end of the tuning coil (E). Connect the terminals of the detector (D and D1) to the phone binding posts (P and P1). Connect the GROUND binding post to one of the condenser terminals (C2) and to the connector (C1) under the lower slider (S2). Connect the other terminal of the condenser (C3) to detector terminal (D). Connect the other detector terminal (D1) to the connector (C) under the upper slider (S1).

Operating the Receiver. Connect a telephone receiver or a radio headset to the PHONE binding posts. Connect an antenna to the ANTENNA binding post and the ground to the GROUND binding post. Test the detector to insure that it is in proper adjustment. Move the sliders (one at a time) until you find the position on the tuning coil where they bring in loudest the signals to which you wish to listen.

HOW TO BUILD A RADIO RECEIVER
WITH A CRYSTAL DETECTOR AND A COUPLER

The device called a coupler makes a better tuner than a tuning coil. A coupler consists of two coils. One coil contains more turns of wire than the other and is called the primary. The primary is connected to the aerial and ground. It is tuned with a slider. The secondary contains fewer turns of wire and is connected to the detector. It is tuned with a variable condenser. There is no direct electrical connection between the primary and secondary. They form a transformer. High frequency currents in the primary induce high frequency currents in the

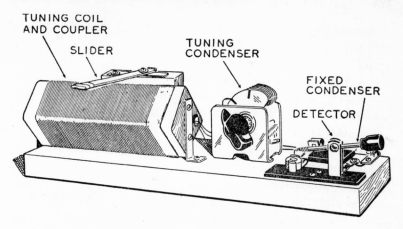

TUNING COIL
AND COUPLER

SLIDER

TUNING
CONDENSER

FIXED
CONDENSER

DETECTOR

RADIO RECEIVER TUNED BY A COUPLER
AND VARIABLE CONDENSER

This is the best of the three receivers described in this chapter. It has greater range and better tuning than the others.

secondary by the process called electromagnetic induction.

Couplers were very popular with amateur wireless experimenters who used crystal detectors in the early days of radio. The instrument they used was called a "loose coupler." The secondary coil of the loose coupler could be moved in and out of the primary coil, in fact moved several inches away from it when necessary. This adjustment was called varying the coupling and aided in tuning the receiver. Loose couplers were usually purchased ready made or built from factory made parts which were available at that time. Such parts are not manufactured today. For that reason and also because it is the purpose of this book to describe only the simplest radio apparatus, the coupler described here is "fixed." The coupling or space between the primary and secondary cannot be varied. The receiver could be tuned better if the coupling was variable but variable coupling would make construction of the receiver difficult for a beginner at building radio apparatus.

LIST OF MATERIALS
REQUIRED TO BUILD A RADIO RECEIVER
WITH A CRYSTAL DETECTOR AND A COUPLER

  1 Wood base 10¾ in. x 5 in. x ¾ in.
  1 Piece of white pine 5¼ in. x 1½ in. x 1½ in.
200 ft. No. 26 B. S. gauge enameled magnet wire
  1 .004 Mfd. mica condenser
  1 150 or 250 mmfd. single gang variable condenser
  1 Knob for variable condenser
  1 Crystal detector
  4 Fahnestock connectors or binding posts
18 No. 5 round head brass screws ½ in. long
  2 No. 5 round head brass screws 1 in. long
  2 Round head 6-32 machine screws ⅝ in. long to fit holes in frame of condenser
20 Brass or copper washers to slip over No. 5 wood screws
  1 Piece galvanized iron sheet 3 in. by 4 in.

Construction.   Dry the base and wood block and give them a coat of shellac. The base is 10¾ in. x 5 in. x ¾ in. The wood block is the same size as that used for the single-slider tuning coil. Make the core for the coupler out of white pine. When finished, it should be 5¼ in. long and 1½ in. by 1½ in. in section. Round the corners slightly with sandpaper. After drying give the core a coat of shellac. The ½ in. dia. holes bored in each end along the axis of the core are for the ½ in. dowel rods which are used when the coupler is wound on the homemade winder. The holes marked A, B, C and D in the drawing of the core are for the terminals of the windings.

Wind the secondary first. It consists of 50 turns of No. 26 B. S. enameled wire wound in a single smooth layer. The small holes B and C communicate with the larger hole D and the ends of the secondary winding are led out through these holes.

When the secondary has been wound wrap one or two layers of thin tough paper around it. Then wind the primary. This is a single layer of No. 26 B. S. enameled wire which starts at the opposite end of the core from the secondary and ends when it has overlapped the secondary about ⅜ in. This end of the primary is the terminal (E) which is connected to the ANTENNA binding post (A). Do not make a mistake and connect the other end of the primary to (A) or the receiver will not operate satisfactorily. The coupler is mounted on the forward left hand corner of the base, supported by two brackets made of sheet metal. One bracket should be the same size and shape as those used to support the single-slider tuner, the other is a straight

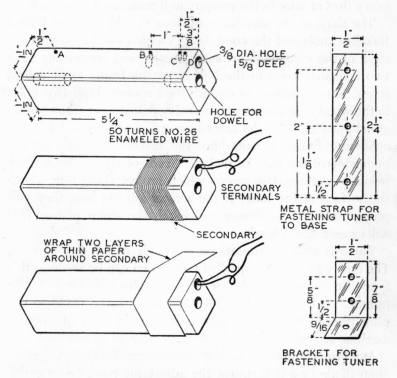

PARTS FOR THE COUPLER

The text explains how to make and wind this part.
These parts are described in the first part of this chapter under the paragraph "The Slider and Other Metal Parts."

metal strip. Use No. 00 sandpaper to remove the enamel insulation from the upper corner of the primary wire so that the slider can make contact with it.

Make a slider and a connector of the same size as used with the single-slider tuner. Pivot the slider on the connector in the center of the wooden block and fasten the block to the base behind the primary. The block is held to the base by two wood screws which pass upward from the underside of the base, through the base and into the block. When the block is set in the correct position the slider can be moved so that it will reach every turn of wire in the primary and make contact with it.

The shaft of the variable condenser should be fitted with a Bakelite knob and the condenser mounted on the base to the right of the coupler. Most small single-gang condensers have two threaded holes in the bottom of the frame to fit a 6-32 screw. Some condensers require 8-32 screws. Drill two holes in the wood base the proper distance apart so that when screws are slipped through the holes they will meet the holes in the condenser frame. Counterbore the holes ¼ in. deep on the underside of the base so that the heads of the screws will be below its surface. Use screws which project about ⅛ in. above the surface of the base. If the screws are too long they will project into the condenser and touch the stator plates. This will cause a short circuit.

There is a small terminal on each side of the stator plates. The only way a good electrical connection can be made to this type of terminal is to slip the end of a wire in the hole in the terminal and solder it there. Connection can be made to the rotor plates by placing a wire under the head of one of the machine screws used to fasten the condenser to the base.

Any type of sensitive crystal detector can be used, a germanium diode or a detector of the adjustable type. For near-by stations, if the greatest signal volume is desired, use a silicon detector. Galena is more sensitive than silicon and will bring in stations from farther away but will not produce signals which

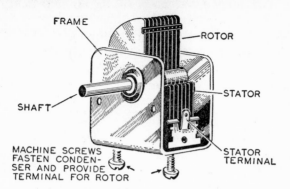

SINGLE GANG VARIABLE CONDENSER

are as loud as those secured from silicon. To bring in distant stations, use a galena detector.

Connect one terminal of the primary (E) to the ANTENNA binding post (A). Connect the slider on the primary to the GROUND binding post (G). Connect one terminal of the secondary (S1) to the terminal on the condenser stator (V1), also to the terminal of the fixed condenser (C1) and to the PHONE binding post (P1).

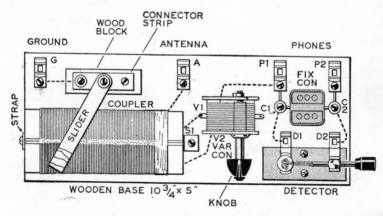

PLAN OF THE RADIO RECEIVER
WITH COUPLER AND CONDENSER TUNING

Connect the other terminal of the secondary (S2) to the condenser rotor and also to the detector terminal (D1). Connect the other terminal of the detector (D2) to the terminal of the fixed condenser (C2) and also to the PHONE binding post (P2).

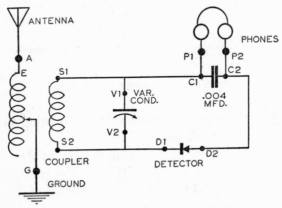

SCHEMATIC CIRCUIT DIAGRAM FOR
HOOKING UP THE COUPLER AND VARIABLE CONDENSER

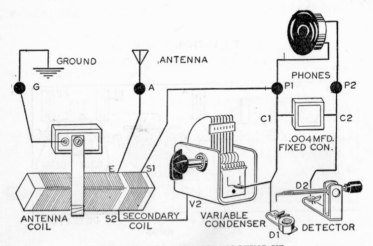

PICTORIAL DIAGRAM FOR HOOKING UP
THE COUPLER AND VARIABLE CONDENSER

To operate the receiver, connect the ANTENNA post (A) to an antenna and the GROUND post (G) to the ground. Connect a radio headset to the PHONE posts (P1 and P2). Adjust the detector and use both the slider and the variable condenser to tune. Turn the variable condenser slowly.

The frequency range of the receiver can be increased by connecting a loading coil and wave-trap to it.

HOW TO BUILD A LOADING COIL AND WAVE TRAP

Neither of the tuning coils described in this chapter are long enough to tune in signals over the entire band of frequencies used by American broadcasting stations. It would be difficult for the average boy to construct the type of slider that is required for longer tuning coils. The problem can be solved by a loading coil, or better still by a loading coil and wave trap. A loading coil is simply a single-slider tuning coil which is connected in series with the antenna and the radio receiver. The loading coil and wave trap combination is a single-slider tuning coil and a variable condenser mounted on a wooden base. This also is connected in series with the antenna and radio receiver.

MATERIALS REQUIRED
FOR CONSTRUCTING A LOADING COIL

   1 Wood base 7½ in. x 4 in. x ¾ in.
   1 Wood block 2½ in. x 2⅛ in. x ¾ in.
125 ft. No. 24 B.S. gauge enameled magnet wire
   1 Piece of galvanized sheet iron approximately 4 in. x 2 in.
   1 Piece No. 14 B. S. bare copper wire 2 in. long
   3 Fahnestock connectors or binding posts
 11 No. 5 round head brass screws ½ in. long
  2 No. 5 round head brass screws 1 in. long
  4 Brass or copper washers to slip over No. 5 wood screws

The parts used in building the loading coil are the same parts used in building the single-slider tuner. The base is

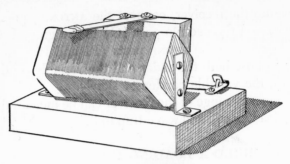

A LOADING COIL

The full name of this instrument is "antenna loading coil." When connected in the antenna circuit of any of the receivers described in this chapter, it is possible to tune in signals of lower frequency than is possible when it is not used.

slightly smaller than the one used for the receiver. Cut the strips used in making the slider, brackets and connector from galvanized iron sheet to the dimensions shown in the illustration of the single-slider tuner. Solder the 2-inch piece of No. 14 bare copper wire to one side of the slider. Wrap the end of the slider which has no hole in it with Scotch tape or adhesive tape to provide an insulated handle for the fingers to touch. The wood block and base should be dried and shellacked.

Wind the tuning coil core with a single layer of No. 24 B. S. enameled wire. Start and finish the winding about ¾ in. from the ends of the core. Use a piece of No. 00 sandpaper to remove the enamel insulation from the wire along one corner of the coil so that the slider can make a good electrical contact.

The plan shows how the parts are assembled on the base. The coil is supported by the two metal brackets. One end of the slider is pivoted on the wood block. The block is fastened to the base by two No. 5 round head screws which pass upward through the bottom of the base and into the block. The heads of the screws are countersunk in the bottom of the base. Use a washer under the head of each screw.

One terminal of the coil (E) is connected to binding post (B). Binding post (A) is connected to the slider.

The loading coil can be used with all of the receivers with crystal detectors. Disconnect the antenna from the ANTENNA binding post on the receiver and connect the antenna to the ANTENNA binding post (A) on the loading coil. Connect binding post (B) on the loading coil to the ANTENNA binding post on the receiver.

To tune in a station move the slider on the loading coil and the slider on the receiver to the positions where the signals desired come in the loudest.

To convert the loading coil into a combination loading coil and wave trap, it is only necessary to connect the terminals of a midget single gang variable condenser to binding posts (A) and (B) on the loading coil. These small condensers cost less than one dollar each. They are made in eight sizes or capacities ranging from 15 micromicrofarads (abbreviated mmfd) to 450

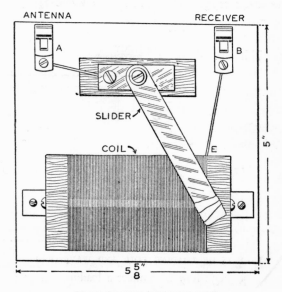

PLAN OF THE LOADING COIL

micromicrofarads. Any of the sizes from 100 mmfd to 450 mmfd can be used for the wave trap. The condenser should be fitted with a Bakelite knob to fit the ¼ in. shaft.

One terminal of the variable condenser is the frame of the condenser. The other terminal is either one of the two small lugs at the sides of the condenser. Connect a wire to one of the lugs by soldering. Connect a wire to the frame by placing the end of the wire under the head of one of the screws which hold the condenser frame to the wood base.

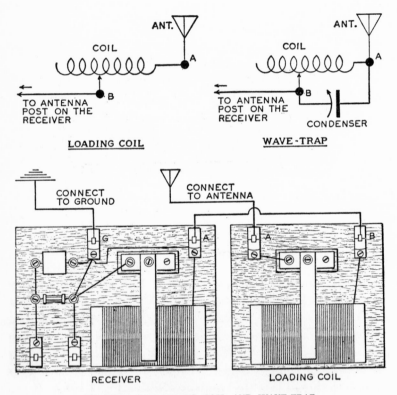

CIRCUITS OF LOADING COIL AND WAVE-TRAP

The bottom sketch shows how to connect a loading coil or a wave-trap to a receiver.

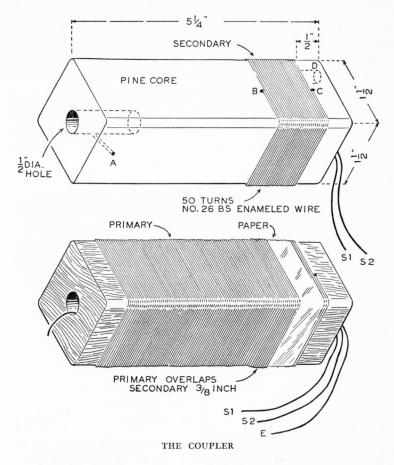

5¼"

SECONDARY

½"

PINE CORE

B   C

D

½"

½"

A

½" DIA.
HOLE

50 TURNS
NO. 26 BS ENAMELED WIRE

PRIMARY   PAPER

S1 S2

PRIMARY OVERLAPS
SECONDARY 3/8 INCH

S1
S2
E

THE COUPLER

It is advisable to make a unit of the coil and condenser by
mounting them on the same base. Use a wooden base about
8 in. x 4 in. x ¾ in. Dry the base and shellac it before using. The
condenser is fastened to the base by two machine screws which
pass upward through the base and into the threaded holes in
the bottom of the condenser. The screws should be just long
enough to thread into the condenser without projecting. If the
screws are long enough to go through the base of the condenser
and touch the stator plates, they will short circuit the condenser

and the unit will not operate. Connect the frame of the condenser to binding post (B). Connect (B) to the end of the loading coil (E). Connect the stator (stationary plates) of the condenser to binding post (A). Connect binding post (A) to the slider.

The combination loading coil and wave trap can be used with all of the receivers with crystal detectors. Disconnect the antenna from the ANTENNA binding post on the receiver and connect the antenna to the ANTENNA binding post (A) on the loading coil. Connect binding post (B) on the loading coil to the ANTENNA binding post on the receiver.

To tune in a station, set the variable condenser at zero. When in this position no portion of the rotor (movable plates) will be interleaved with the stator plates. Then use both sliders (one on the loading coil and one on the tuner) to bring in the signals you wish. If two stations are heard at the same time, adjusting the variable condenser will aid in eliminating the station which is causing interference with the signals you wish to listen to.

A TEST BUZZER FOR ADJUSTING DETECTOR

If you make your own crystal detector, the best way to locate the point of the "cat-whisker" on a sensitive spot of the crystal is to use a test buzzer. To do this, you need a small electric buzzer, a dry cell and a switch. You can use a telegraph key or a push button in place of the switch. An ordinary call buzzer can be used but one of the small buzzers with a high-pitched sound made for code practice is more desirable. Connect the buzzer, dry cell and switch in series so that the buzzer can be operated by closing the switch. Run a wire from the contact post on the buzzer (see illustration) to the ground wire of your crystal set. Connect your headset or phone to their binding posts on the set. Close the switch so as to put the buzzer in operation. Put your headset on, or, if you have a single phone, hold it to your ear. Move the cat-whisker around on the crystal and find the spot where you can hear the buzzer tone the loudest. Adjust the tension of the cat-whisker until it gives the best signal. Then open the switch to stop the buzzer. The detector is now adjusted to receive radio signals. Be careful not to jar or disturb the detector and throw it out of adjustment.

You can use a code-practice set as a test buzzer. Run a wire from the contact post on the buzzer to the ground wire of the crystal set. Press the key so that the buzzer operates while you are locating the point of the cat-whisker on the most sensitive spot of the crystal.

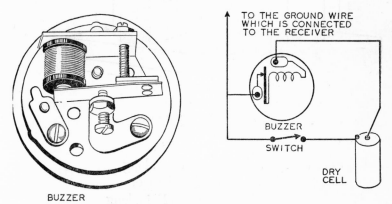

BUZZER

A HIGH PITCHED TEST BUZZER AND THE CIRCUIT
USED FOR TESTING AND ADJUSTING CRYSTAL DETECTORS

HOW TO BUILD A WINDING MACHINE
FOR TUNING COILS AND COUPLERS

The materials required are wood from a packing box, a few screws, a piece of ½ in. dowel rod, a piece of wire from a coat hanger and a clamp. A handsaw, screwdriver, ½-inch auger bit and a No. 28 twist drill will be needed to make the parts.

PARTS REQUIRED FOR THE WINDER

1 Wood base 8 in. x 3¾ in. x ½ in.
2 Wood uprights 4½ in. x 2¼ in. x ½ in.

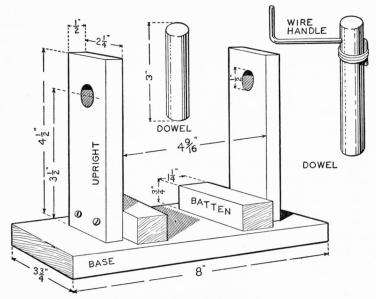

PARTS FOR THE WINDER COIL

2 Wood battens 3½ in. x 1¼ in. x ¾ in.
2 Pieces ½-in. dia. maple dowel 3 in. long
1 Piece of steel wire from a coat hanger
8 No. 6 round head wood screws 1¼ in. long

Cut the wooden parts to the dimensions shown in the illustration. Dry them and shellac them. Bore a ½-in. diameter hole through both uprights on their center line and 3½ in. from an end.

Make two holes in each upright with a No. 28 twist drill. The holes should be ⅜ in. from the end and at the end opposite the ½ in. hole. Slip a No. 6 wood screw through each of the small holes in the uprights and fasten each upright to a batten. Fasten each batten to the base using two screws which pass upward through the base from the underside. Use the No. 28 holes to drill through the base for the screws. Countersink the heads of the screws. The battens should be located so that the distance between the uprights is ⅛ in. longer than the core which is to be wound. The ½ in. diameter hole in the uprights are bearings and must be in line so that a piece of ½ in. diameter dowel passing through both holes will turn freely. Fasten one upright and batten to the base. Then slip the dowel through the bearing holes in both uprights and fasten the second batten to the base at the proper distance. Assembling the winder with the dowel shaft in the bearing holes will bring the holes into line.

A piece of steel wire (from a coat hanger) is slipped through a hole near the end of one of the dowels and bent to form a crank. This wire handle is used to turn the core when winding it. The dowel shafts should turn freely in the bearing holes in the uprights. If they are hard to turn, free them by sandpapering the dowels to make them slightly smaller.

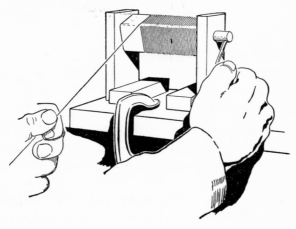

WINDING A TUNING COIL

CHAPTER NINE

HOW TO BUILD
A ONE-TUBE REGENERATIVE RECEIVER

None of the receivers with crystal detectors in this book are elaborate. They are not difficult to make and the parts and materials required for their construction do not cost much. These are good designs for the boy who is building a radio receiver for the first time. Their only disadvantage is that sometimes they will bring in more than one station simultaneously. A more sensitive and more selective receiver can be built by using a vacuum tube detector in a feedback or regenerative circuit.

If you have read Chapter Four you will remember that regeneration in a radio circuit consists of feeding back current from the plate circuit to the grid circuit. Regeneration in a receiver greatly strengthens and amplifies signals.

The one-tube regenerative receiver described in this chapter will bring in the signals of amateur, police, aviation, ship and broadcast stations from stations hundreds of miles away. It responds to a wider range of frequencies and tunes more sharply than any of the crystal detector receivers. It utilizes a "low drain" vacuum tube which consumes very little current and so is especially suited to operation on batteries. When provided with a complete set of plug-in coils, the receiver will tune in all wavelengths from 16 to 550 meters. It will produce

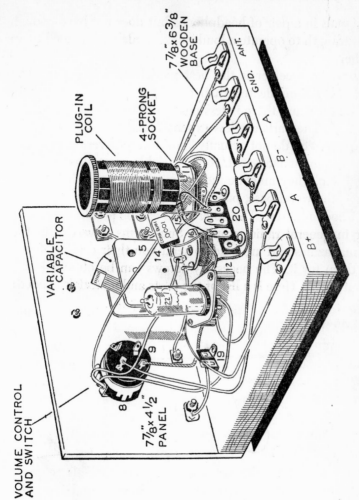

VOLUME CONTROL
AND SWITCH

VARIABLE
CAPACITOR

PLUG-IN
COIL

4-PRONG
SOCKET

7⅞″×6⅜″
WOODEN
BASE

ANT.

GND.

A

B−

A

B+

7⅞″×4½″
PANEL

ONE-TUBE REGENERATIVE RECEIVER

The receiver viewed from the back of the panel. The numerals can be used to identify the parts. The same numerals are used in connection with the same parts in the list of parts and the circuit diagrams.

loud signals in a pair of headphones but does not have enough signal strength to operate a loudspeaker unless connected to an amplifier.

A one-tube receiver is the best model for a beginner. The circuit is less complicated than that of a receiver using more than one tube and there is less chance of making a mistake in the wiring. The parts are less expensive and can be assembled more easily. You do not actually "build" a receiver of this type. A boy cannot make satisfactory variable capacitors, volume controls, etc. They must be factory made. The only homemade parts are the wood base, panel, ground plate, connecting strips and a wooden bolster. The other parts can be purchased from a dealer in general radio supplies. Such firms advertise in the radio magazines and are glad to send you their catalog if you write them for it. The necessary screws can be obtained at a hardware store. Here is a list of the parts and materials needed:

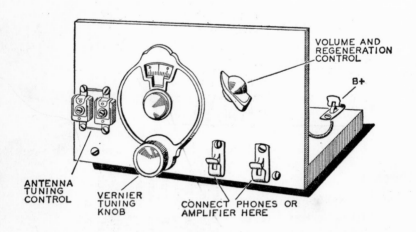

ANTENNA
TUNING
CONTROL

VERNIER
TUNING
KNOB

CONNECT PHONES OR
AMPLIFIER HERE

VOLUME AND
REGENERATION
CONTROL

B+

ONE-TUBE REGENERATIVE RECEIVER

The receiver from the front of the panel. This view reveals parts which cannot be seen in the preceding sketch.

1 6BF6 Receiving tube (22)

1 Wood base 7⅞ in. x 6⅜ in. x ¾ in. (2)

1 Wood panel 7⅞ in. x 4½ in. x ¼ in. (3)

1 Piece of wood 1 in. x 2½ in. x ¼ in. to be used as a bolster for the variable capacitor * if necessary

5 Connecting strips 1⅛ in. x ⅜ in. cut from thin sheet metal

1 Piece of thin sheet metal 7¼ in. x 5¾ in.

1 500,000-ohm volume control (8)

1 Switch to fit volume control (9)

1 Knob for volume control (10)

1 Vernier knob and dial (6)

2 4-prong plug-in coils for broadcast band when used with a 365-MMFD tuning capacitor

1 10 to 365-MMFD variable tuning capacitor

1 4-prong socket (77)

1 Socket for 7-pin 6BF6 tube (12)

2 4-80 MMFD-mica trimmer capacitors (7)

1 2.5-millihenry radio frequency choke (16)

1 2.2-megohm ¼ watt resistor (15)

1 .0001-MFD mica capacitor (14)

1 .0025-MFD mica capacitor (13)

1 6-volt battery or 6.3-volt filament transformer

1 67½- or 90-volt B battery

8 Binding posts or Fahnestock connectors (17)

1 Single-terminal Bakelite terminal strip (19)

1 Three-terminal Bakelite terminal strip (20)

14 ⅝-in. No. 6 round head brass wood screws

4 ½-in. 6-32 round head brass machine screws with brass nuts to fit

2 ¾-in. 6-32 round head brass machine screws

1 2000-ohm radio headset

4 Rubber head tacks; 8 Small tacks

Shellac, sandpaper, rosin-core solder, push-back wire

4 Round head screws and spacers for mounting sockets

* Let's call condensers by their accurate scientific name from now on.

The numbers in parentheses following some of the items in the list on page 163 identify these parts on the plan and in the wiring diagrams.

DESCRIPTION OF SOME OF THE PARTS

The Tube. When this book was first published, small low-current-consuming triode tubes for use in battery-operated receivers as detectors and amplifiers were manufactured. They are no longer available. The triode used in the one-tube regenerative receiver described in this chapter and in the amplifiers in the chapter following is the triode section of a 6BF6 tube. The 6BF6 is a multi-unit tube technically described as a twin

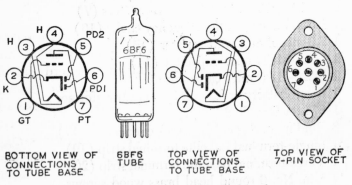

BOTTOM VIEW OF   6BF6   TOP VIEW OF   TOP VIEW OF
CONNECTIONS   TUBE   CONNECTIONS   7-PIN SOCKET
TO TUBE BASE   TO TUBE BASE

BASING DIAGRAMS AND SOCKET FOR 6BF6 TUBE

diode and medium-mu triode. It is a miniature type normally used as a combined detector, amplifier and automatic volume control (avc) tube. It consists of a triode (three elements) and two diodes (two elements) in the same glass envelope. Only the triode section is used by the regenerative receiver and by the amplifiers. The tube requires a miniature seven-contact socket and may be mounted in any position. Only five of the contact pins (Nos. 1, 2, 3, 4 and 7) are used in the apparatus described in this book.

6BF6 has no filament. A filament in a tube usually serves both as a cathode and a source of heat. 6BF6 has a cathode (pin No. 2) and a heater (pins Nos. 3 and 4) common to the triode and diodes. The heater is designed to be operated on 6.3 volts. Either AC or DC may be used. The heater current is 0.3 amperes at 6.3 volts.

Current Supply. Four new size D flashlight cells or four new No. 6 dry cells connected in series will operate the heater of a 6BF6 tube. The voltage of four new dry cells in series will be slightly more than 6 volts. The voltage will drop with use and with age. When the voltage of four cells drops below 5½ volts the tube will probably not function well. A set of No. 6 dry cells will outlast many size D flashlight cells discharged at an 0.3 ampere rate.

The most satisfactory source of 6.3-volt heater current is a small 6.3-volt filament transformer. The primary of the transformer should be connected to an attachment cord and plug which can be plugged into a 117-volt AC outlet. The secondary is connected to contacts 3 and 4 on the socket. The transformer which you buy may be one which has three wires connected to the primary and three to the secondary. The electric wiring in many homes with a two-wire feeder is inadequate. The result is that when lamps, radios, etc. are turned on the line voltage is only 105 to 107 volts. An adequate wiring system with a three-wire feeder supplies current at 117 to 120 volts. The black primary wire and the black yellow wire are used when the house voltage is approximately 107. When 117 to 120 volts current is available, the black and the red and black primary wires are used. The green and yellow secondary wire is a "center tap." It, together with either one of the green wires will deliver 6.3 volts if the correct pair of primary wires are connected to the lighting circuit.

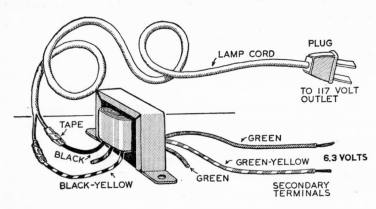

LAMP CORD

PLUG

TO 117 VOLT OUTLET

TAPE

GREEN

BLACK

GREEN-YELLOW   6.3 VOLTS

GREEN

BLACK-YELLOW

SECONDARY TERMINALS

6.3-VOLT FILAMENT TRANSFORMER

Sockets.   Eby one-piece molded Bakelite sockets for the tube and coil can be mounted more easily than other types. They can be fastened directly to the wood base with two screws. Amphenol "MIP" sockets and Eby wafer sockets made of laminated Bakelite cost less than other sockets. They can be used if mounted on spacers which raise them about ⅜ inch above the base.

The Volume and Regeneration Control.   This should be the type to which a switch can be attached. Purchase a switch also. The switch is connected in series with the tube filament and the battery which heats the filament. Then the same knob which controls the volume and regeneration can be used to turn the receiver on and off.

Variable Capacitor.   Purchase a standard midget single gang TRF type variable capacitor with two bearings. It is more rugged than a single bearing capacitor. The maximum capacity should be 365 micromicrofarads (abbreviated MMFD) and the minimum when the plates are not intermeshed about 10 MMFD. TRF is the abbreviation for "tuned radio frequency."

There is space for trimmers provided on the TRF capacitors but trimmers are not used at that point in the circuit of a regenerative receiver. Small rotary variable capacitors are usually so built that the capacity increases when the shaft is turned in a counterclockwise direction. The shaft can be rotated 180°.

Capacitors are sometimes listed in catalogs as condensers. Capacitor is a better term and is gradually replacing the older word.

The Dial and Knob. Any of several types of knobs which fit a ¼-inch round shaft can be used to turn the variable capacitor. Some are equipped with pointers designed to swing over a dial plate attached to the panel. Others have a dial which moves with the knob and a marker on the panel indicates the position of the dial. It is difficult to make a close adjustment of the variable capacitor with any of these direct drives. A

VERNIER DIAL

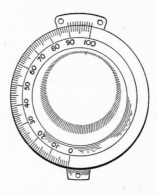

BAKELITE KNOB AND DIAL

TUNING DIALS AND KNOBS

The knob and dial at the right is a direct drive device. Any rotation of the knob moves the tuning capacitor an equal amount. The vernier knob and dial is an indirect drive. The knob and dial are geared to the capacitor so that the knob must be turned a considerable distance in order to turn the capacitor a short distance.

vernier dial is more satisfactory. It should have a 0-180° counterclockwise scale to fit the capacitor. The knob on a vernier dial does not drive the condenser shaft directly. It is geared. The knob on the type of vernier dial in the illustration must be turned several revolutions in order to turn the condenser shaft one-half revolution. This permits very fine adjustment of the condenser and close tuning.

Trimmer Capacitors. Trimmer and padder capacitors are commonly used in radio receivers to adjust circuits which include radio frequency transformers and variable capacitors. In the one-tube regenerative receiver, two trimmer capacitors connected in parallel are used to tune the antenna circuit. They are adjusted with a screwdriver. It is necessary to use a different adjustment for each plug-in coil.

A small variable capacitor which has a capacity range of 10 to 200 micromicrofarads can be used in place of the two trimmer capacitors. It is easier to adjust (adjustment is made by turning a knob) than trimmer capacitors but costs five times as much as a pair of trimmer capacitors. Trimmer capacitors are used in the one-tube regenerative receiver to keep the cost low.

The Plug-in Coils. It is advisable to purchase factory made plug-in coils for the receiver. Several mail order firms sell completed coils and also unwound coil forms. 4-prong, 5-prong and 6-prong coils are available but only 4-prong coils will fit this one-tube regenerative receiver. Each 4-prong plug-in coil consists of two separate windings wound on a molded Bakelite form. The terminals of the windings are connected to the prongs. The prongs fit the standard 4-prong tube socket. The upper (and longer) winding is called the antenna and grid coil. The lower and smaller winding is the "tickler" coil.

The size of the coils plugged into the 4-prong socket determines the frequency range of the receiver. You will need two readymade 4-prong plug-in coils with proper windings so that when used with a 365-MMFD tuning condenser, the frequency

band of the receiver will cover the broadcast band. Coils covering the higher frequencies or shorter wavelengths are also obtainable.

During war time some radio parts are scarce and it is difficult to find readymade plug-in coils. It may be necessary then to buy empty coil forms and wind them. The method of winding is described later in this chapter.

The Homemade Parts.　The base of the receiver is a piece of pine 7⅞ in. x 6⅜ in. x ¾ in. Smooth it with sandpaper and finish all surfaces including the underside with two coats of white shellac. The shellac will seal the wood against moisture and reduce its tendency to warp. The panel is a piece of ply-

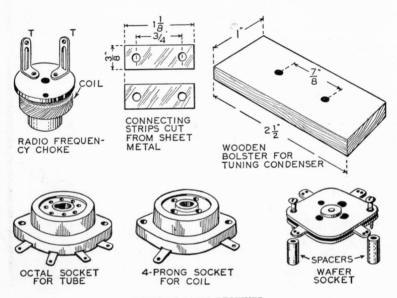

RADIO FREQUEN-
CY CHOKE

CONNECTING
STRIPS CUT
FROM SHEET
METAL

WOODEN
BOLSTER FOR
TUNING CONDENSER

OCTAL SOCKET
FOR TUBE

4-PRONG SOCKET
FOR COIL

WAFER
SOCKET

SPACERS

PARTS FOR THE RECEIVER

Two connecting strips are used to connect the trimmer condensers in parallel. Three of the connecting strips are used as terminals. Use one under each of the nuts on the back of the panel which hold the PHONE posts, and one to make connection to the frame of the tuning capacitor. The two sockets at the lower left are Eby sockets. The letter "T" indicates the terminals on the high-frequency choke.

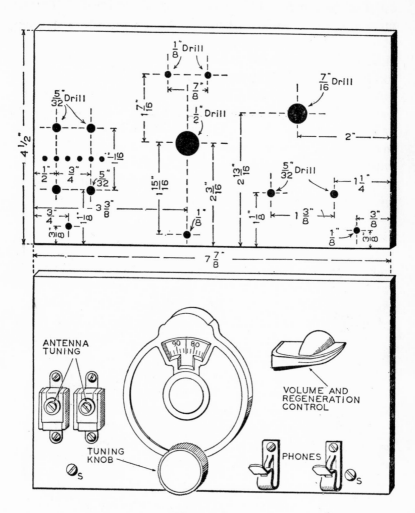

THE PANEL

The panel is made of ¼ in. to ⅜ in. plywood, drilled as shown in the top drawing. The drawing at the bottom shows the front of the panel after the parts have been mounted on it. The position of the holes drilled in the panel and used to mount the capacitors and dial may differ from the locations shown in the upper sketch. They should be located to fit the particular capacitors and dial which you use.

wood measuring 7⅞ in. x 4½ in. The thickness is unimportant. Plywood ranging from ¼ in. to ⅜ in. thick will make a satisfactory panel. The panel should be shellacked on both sides and all edges. It is fastened to one edge of the base by three No. 6 round head brass wood screws (marked S in illustration).

The ground plate is a piece of thin sheet metal (galvanized iron or tinplate) 7¼ in. x 5¾ in. It can be cut out of a one-gallon can with a pair of snips. Cut a small piece off each corner so as to eliminate the sharp points. Flatten the metal by pounding it with a block of wood and then punch eight small holes, one in each corner and one near each edge midway from the corner, with the point of a small nail.

The ground plate is fastened to the underside of the base by eight small tacks which pass through the holes punched in it with a nail. If the receiver is equipped with the type of variable capacitor which must be fastened to the base, the ground plate cannot be attached to the base until after the capacitor has been mounted. If a panel-mounted capacitor is used, the ground plate can be attached before the panel is put in place.

The ground plate reduces "body effect." This is a disturbance in the tuning which may take place when a hand is moved either toward or away from the receiver.

If a panel-mounting variable capacitor is used, it will not be necessary to make a small wood bolster. This 2½ in. x 1 in. x ¼ in. wood strip is required only for a base-mounting variable capacitor. The holes in the bolster should be the same distance apart as the mounting holes in the condenser so they will align.

ASSEMBLING THE RECEIVER

The plan of the receiver in one of the illustrations is the best guide for assembling the parts on the base and panel. At the top is a scale for use in determining the exact location of the parts. This scale can be used to measure inches in the same

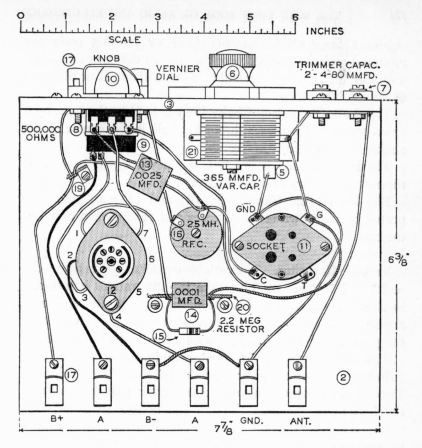

PLAN OF THE RECEIVER

manner as the scale on a map is used to measure distance in miles. For example, to determine the exact location of the center of the tube socket (12), measure the distance on the plan from the left hand edge of the base to the center of the socket and from the back edge of the base to the center of the socket. Use a ruler, a pair of dividers or a strip of paper to measure these distances, whichever is convenient, and then compare them with the scale. This will show the center of the socket to be 2⅛ in. from the left hand edge and 3½ in. from the back edge.

The Fahnestock Connectors (17) or binding posts are mounted near the back edge of the base so that wires from the batteries, etc., can be attached to them without disturbing any of the receiver wiring.

The Radio-Frequency Choke (16) is held to the base by a BRASS screw which passes through a hole in the center of the choke. Do not use an iron screw.

The Resistor (15) is not fastened down to the base. It is supported by its own terminal wires.

The Mica Fixed Capacitors (14) and (13) are also supported by their own terminal wires and not fastened down to the base.

Variable Capacitor.　The variable capacitor (5) in the model receiver which was used to make the illustrations is fastened to the wooden base close to the panel. At first glance, it may appear to be supported on the panel. The shaft extends through the panel but the capacitor rests on a small wood bolster strip (21) which measures approximately 2½ in. x 1 in. x 14 in. The strip rests on the base, between the base and the condenser. Two ¾-inch, 6-32 round head machine screws pass upward from the bottom of the base through the bolster strip and into threaded holes in the bottom of the capacitor frame. The underside of the base is counterbored ⅜-inch deep so that the heads of the screws are below the surface and cannot come into contact with the ground plate. The screws should not be long enough to project through the capacitor frame more than 1/16 inch. If too long they will touch the stator plates and short circuit the capacitor.

Some variable capacitors are designed to be mounted on a panel. If you obtain a capacitor of that type, you will not need to make a bolster strip. Bore a hole in the panel just large enough to pass the threaded bearing. Push the bearing through the hole from the rear of the panel and place the threaded nut on the bearing from the front. Tighten the nut until the capacitor is pulled firmly against the rear of the panel.

To Mount a Vernier Knob and Dial. Screws, nuts and a paper mounting template are packed with each vernier dial of the type shown in the illustrations.

1.   Place the mounting template on the panel so that its center coincides with the center of the variable capacitor shaft.

2.   Use a sharp scriber or a prick punch to mark all hole centers through the template onto the panel.

3.   Remove the template and drill the holes of the diameter specified on the template.

4.   If the capacitor shaft projects more than ⅞ inch beyond the front of the panel cut the surplus length off with a hacksaw.

5.   Remove the hub cap from the dial by pulling it out.

6.   Slip the dial over the end of the capacitor shaft that projects through the panel and fasten it in place by means of the four small screws, lock washers and nuts furnished with the dial.

7.   Set the capacitor at its zero or position of minimum capacity and rotate the dial until it also is at zero before tightening the set-screw.

8.   Tighten the hub set-screw but when doing this make certain that the dial disk is pushed back far enough so that it does not rub against the inside of the dial casing.

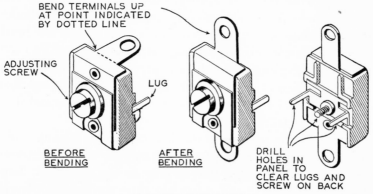

BEND TERMINALS UP
AT POINT INDICATED
BY DOTTED LINE

ADJUSTING
SCREW

LUG

BEFORE
BENDING

AFTER
BENDING

DRILL
HOLES IN
PANEL TO
CLEAR LUGS AND
SCREW ON BACK

TRIMMER CAPACITORS

Holes must be drilled in the panel and the terminals on the trimmer capacitors must be bent as shown in the illustration before the capacitors can be mounted.

9. Replace the hub cap by pushing it into place.

The drive ratio of the vernier dial is variable. It provides 6 to 1 gearing in the fast position and 20 to 1 gearing in the slow position. Intermediate ratios can be selected by proper positioning of the small metal ball directly above the tuning knob.

How to Attach the Switch to the Volume Control.   Pry off the removable portion of the metal cover on the volume control. Hold the control in your left hand so that the shaft points toward you. Use your right hand to turn the shaft in a clockwise direction as far as it will go.

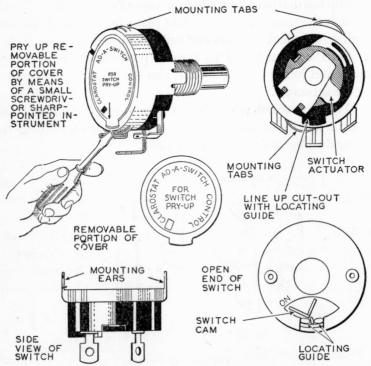

HOW TO ATTACH THE SWITCH TO THE VOLUME CONTROL

This is described fully in the text.

Notice that there are two projecting metal tabs or "ears" on the metal rim of the switch—also that there is an opening in the switch cover. Inside the switch and visible through the opening is a "V"-shaped cam. Moving the cam operates the switch. Move the cam until it is in the center of the opening. Line up the projecting ears on the switch housing with the metal guides in the control case. Then press the switch firmly against the control and while holding it in that position bend the ears so that the switch cannot slip away from the control.

The control is mounted on the back of the wood panel with the shaft projecting from the front of the panel. Drill a hole in the panel just large enough so that the shaft bushing will pass through. Slip the bushing into the hole from the back of the panel and put the nut on from the front. Tighten the nut until the control is held firmly against the panel. Before tightening the nut turn the control so that the terminals are at the top.

The shaft provided on the control will probably prove to be longer than is necessary and it must be cut off so that the control knob will be close to the panel. If the shaft is the notched type, it can be shortened by holding it in a pair of pliers and breaking it at the notch which will reduce it to the correct length. If the shaft is not notched, cut off the surplus length with a fine tooth hacksaw.

Fasten a molded Bakelite knob of the set screw type to the control shaft. Slip the "U"-shaped adapter which comes with the control over the end of the shaft. Loosen the set screw in the knob until it will not prevent the knob from sliding on the shaft. Set the knob where it belongs and tighten the set screw with a small screwdriver.

WIRING THE RECEIVER

When all parts have been fastened in position on the panel and base, the receiver is ready for wiring. Use push-back wire for the connections. The ends of all wires except those which can be clamped firmly under a screw or nut should be soldered with rosin core solder only. Acid core solder may cause short circuits which will prevent the receiver from operating. Instruction in soldering is found in another chapter at the end of this book.

The schematic circuit diagram, pictorial circuit diagram and the plan show how to make the connections. Have a pencil handy and as each connection is made, make a check mark alongside the equivalent connection on the circuit diagrams and plan. Check each connection in this manner and it will help to insure that none are overlooked. The wires should be as short as possible. Some wires in the plan are shown longer than is necessary from the standpoint of good wiring. They were drawn that way so that each wire can be traced from one end to the other. Follow the circuit diagrams and the plan with the utmost care. After completing the wiring, check it

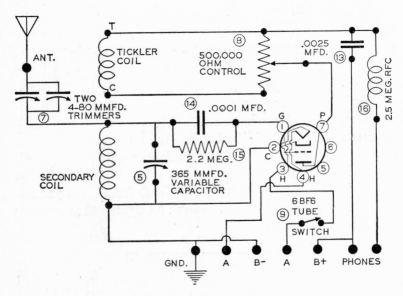

SCHEMATIC CIRCUIT DIAGRAM
FOR THE ONE-TUBE REGENERATIVE RECEIVER

carefully the second time. If a single wire is omitted or connected to the wrong place the receiver will not operate. The black wires in the plan are filament circuit connections.

HOW TO OPERATE THE RECEIVER

When the wiring is complete and has been checked, the receiver is ready for use.

Connect a 2,000-ohm radio headset to the PHONE terminals on the front of the panel. Place a type 6BF6 tube in the tube socket (12) and a 4-prong broadcast coil in the 4-prong socket (11). Mark the wooden base near each terminal so that the terminals can be readily identified as in the plan. Connect an antenna to the ANT terminal and a ground wire to the GND terminal.

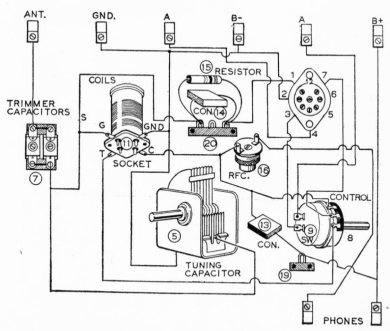

PICTORIAL CIRCUIT DIAGRAM
FOR THE ONE-TUBE REGENERATIVE RECEIVER

The antenna should be a 50-75 foot horizontal wire carefully insulated from surrounding objects.

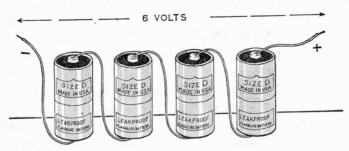

Four size D flashlight cells connected in series will operate the heater in a 6BF6 tube, but No. 6 dry cells will give much longer service.

A 6-volt A battery or a 6.3-volt filament transformer and a 67½-volt B battery are required. The terminals on a B battery may require a three-prong plug or a pair of snap-ons in order to connect them to the receiver. If they are the type which requires a plug, solder two wires about 12 inches long to the plug terminals marked positive and negative. If snap-on terminals are provided solder a male snap-on to a 12 inch length of flexible wire and a female snap-on to a second wire of the same length. Connect the free ends of the wires to the B— and B+ terminals. This must be done correctly because the receiver will not operate if the positive wire is connected to the

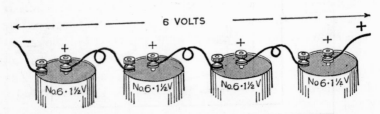

FOUR NO. 6 DRY CELLS CONNECTED IN SERIES

These large cells cost much more than size D cells but are more economical if the regenerative receiver or amplifiers are used frequently.

terminal intended for the negative wire and vice versa. It is of no importance how the terminals of the transformer or of a 6-volt battery are connected to the A terminals. The center terminal on a flashlight cell and on a No. 6 dry cell are positive. The terminals on a B battery are marked with plus $(+)$ and $(-)$ signs to indicate respectively positive and negative.

Adjust the headset to fit your ears snugly. Then turn the regeneration control knob in a clockwise direction so as to close the filament switch and light the tube. Allow a few seconds to pass so that the tube warms up. Then turn the regeneration control knob until a distinct hiss is heard in the phones. The hissing sound is called "spilling over." With the set spilling over, adjust the trimmer capacitors (7) with a screwdriver. This can be done most satisfactorily with a non-metallic screwdriver, a fiber screwdriver used by radio service men and called an alignment tool. Turn the adjusting screw on each of the trimmer condensers in a clockwise direction until it will go no farther. Then turn it two or three complete turns in the reverse direction (counterclockwise). Adjust both condensers very slowly, turning the alignment tool first in one direction and then in the other until you find the adjustment which produces the loudest hiss in the headphones. Slowly rotate the knob on the tuning capacitor and as the capacitor turns a series of whistles and squeals will be heard, each indicating a different broadcast station. Turn the tuning knob until a spot is found where a continuous whistle can be heard and where it is loudest. The whistle can now be eliminated and replaced by signals from a radio station by a slight adjustment of the regeneration control. Turn the control counterclockwise until all whistling and hissing stops and radio signals can be heard. The volume of the signals can be regulated by the regeneration control.

When a station has been tuned in and the signal strength adjusted, a slight readjustment of the tuning control may be necessary. If signals are weak and whistling sounds do not disappear when the regeneration control is turned back almost to the off position, try tightening the adjusting screws on the trimmer capacitors.

When you have learned how to tune in stations in the broadcast band, you may wish to listen to stations on other frequencies—police, amateur, ship-to-shore, etc. Remove the broadcast band coil from the 4-prong socket and replace it with a coil intended for the frequencies you are interested in. The trimmer condensers must be adjusted for each coil. The adjustment of the trimmers need not be close, except for weak signals. Weak signals require careful and close adjustment of all three controls, namely; the tuning capacitor, the trimmer capacitors and the regeneration control. Careful tuning is required to bring in signals from amateur stations. The frequency of an amateur station is always much higher than that of a broadcast station. Amateur stations operate on much lower power than broadcast stations and their signals must be built up by careful adjustment of the receiver controls. It requires some experience and skill to tune the receiver so as to secure its best performance. So don't expect to pick up stations all over the world the first time you have the set in operation.

Signals from broadcasting and amateur radiotelephone stations come in best when the regeneration control is adjusted just below the point where whistling is produced. Telegraph signals ("dits and dahs") from code stations come in best when the regeneration control is adjusted just above the point where whistling is produced.

TROUBLE SHOOTING

Suppose that you have completed your receiver, hooked it up according to directions but do not pick up any signals. What then? You will have to go trouble shooting and find the cause. There are several things to do which may locate the trouble.

1. Disconnect the headphones from the PHONE post and touch

the terminals of the phone cord to the terminals of the filament (A) battery. If you do not hear a click each time you make and break the circuit, there is a loose or broken connection in the phone cord or in the receivers.

2.   Turn the volume control switch so that the tube heater is lighted. Disconnect the positive B battery wire from the B+ binding post on the receiver. Tap the bare end of the wire against the B+ post and listen in the headphones. If you do not hear distinct clicks in the headphones, there is a connection missing or broken. Look for it.

If clicks can be heard in the headphones when you disconnect the B battery, it is a good omen and you can proceed to test other parts of the receiver.

If no whistles or squeals are heard in the headphones when a broadcast coil is in the coil socket and the tuning control and regeneration control are moved back and forth (as far as they will go), the receiver is not regenerating.

1.   The trimmer capacitors may be set up too tight to permit the receiver to regenerate. Loosen the adjusting screws on both capacitors and try tuning the receiver again.

2.   If the receiver will not regenerate and produce squealing and whistling sounds when the controls are moved, check all connections and also check the batteries. Both A and B batteries should be fresh and connected properly.

3.   Examine the variable tuning capacitor. Check it carefully. Make certain that there is no dirt, a small piece of wire or metal between the plates and short circuiting the rotor and stator.

4.   Failure to regenerate may be caused by a tickler coil winding which is reversed. It is then necessary to reverse the connections which lead from the regeneration control to the coil socket. Unsolder the wires connected to the socket terminals marked T and C in the plan and solder to T the wire formerly connected to C. The wire formerly attached to T should be soldered to C. Do not make this change, however, until it is

certain that failure of the receiver to regenerate is not due to other causes.

HOW TO WIND A PLUG-IN COIL

Smooth and ribbed molded Bakelite coil forms of several lengths and diameters are listed in radio catalogs. To make the coils for the one-tube regenerative receiver which will enable it to tune in the broadcasting frequencies, buy two 4-prong, smooth rim coil forms, either 1¼ inches or 1⅜ inches in diameter and with a winding space 2⅛ inches long. About 75 feet of No. 34 B.S. gauge enameled wire and 35 feet of No. 30 B.S. gauge are also required. A ¼-lb. spool of each size is the smallest quantity sold and is more than sufficient.

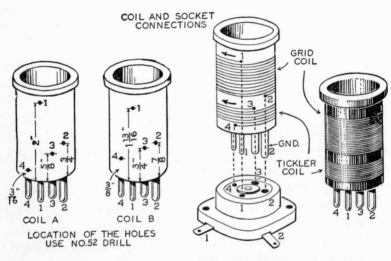

COILS FOR THE BROADCAST BAND

The forms must be drilled so that the ends of the windings can pass through to the prongs. The left-hand sketches show the distance of the holes from the bottom of the forms. The holes can be spaced farther apart around the circumference of the form so that each is above its corresponding prong. The holes and corresponding prongs are marked with the same numerals in the illustration.

Four holes to anchor the ends of the windings must be drilled through the side of each form. The location of the holes is indicated in one of the illustrations. Bore the holes with a No. 52 twist drill held in a drill press or hand drill. The drill may have a tendency to slip away from the spot where a hole is to be made. This difficulty can be avoided by marking the spots where the holes are to be drilled and making a small indentation at each of these spots with the point of a penknife. Twist the knife blade until the point makes an indentation in the Bakelite form deep enough so that when the point of the drill is placed in it, the drill will not slip or "walk" away.

When all four holes have been drilled, turn the coil form so that the prongs point toward you and the two large prongs are at the bottom. Mark the prongs 1, 2, 3, 4, starting with the upper right hand small prong and proceeding in a clockwise direction. Use the point of a penknife blade to scratch the numerals on the base close to the prongs exactly as shown in the illustration. Notice that the upper left hand prong (one of the small ones) is No. 1; the lower left hand prong (large) is marked 2, etc. It is necessary for these numbers to correspond with those in the illustration or the circuit will be incorrect and the receiver will not operate.

Wind 150 turns of No. 34 on the grid coil (upper winding) and 45 turns on the tickler coil (lower winding). Use No. 30 B. S. enamel for coil B. Wind 70 turns on the grid coil (upper winding) and 20 turns on the tickler coil (lower winding). Wind all the coils in the direction indicated by the arrow in the illustration.

Chapter Ten

YOU CAN BUILD AN AMPLIFIER

Lee De Forest soon discovered that his audion tube was not only a good detector for wireless telegraph signals—it was also a wonderful amplifier of amperes and volts. A tiny, almost immeasurably small current fed to the grid of the tube would cause a much greater current to flow in the plate circuit. In this way a few electrons could control a great procession of other electrons. At first the amplifier was used principally to intensify wireless telegraph signals. Weak signals, hardly audible in the headphones, could be intensified and heard several feet away from the phones. Next it became a telephone "repeater." Before 1914 the longest distance it was practical to telephone was about 1,000 miles. The tiny electrical impulses carrying the voice over telephone wires were lost in travelling the distance from New York to Denver unless the copper wires were one-half inch in diameter. Some practical method of boosting and amplifying the feeble currents was necessary to make transcontinental telephony possible. The American Telephone and Telegraph Company bought the audion patent from De Forest for $50,000.00. The scientists and engineers of the Bell laboratories soon found how to improve the tube and use it as a telephone amplifier (called a "repeater" when used in telephony). Telephony across the continent was made a comparatively simple matter. Today it is possible to talk between any two places where wires can be stretched. Vacuum tube amplifiers are a necessary part of the present telephone system. On a coast to coast call, the currents controlled by your voice pass through thousands of tubes.

The vacuum tube amplifier proved to be one of the most important inventions of the twentieth century. It is an essential part of all radio, radar and television transmitters and receivers, of the telephone system and of almost unnumbered laboratory instruments.

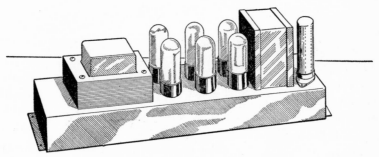

AN ELECTRONIC AMPLIFIER

The amplifier is one of the most useful inventions of the past century. It is an essential part of modern radio, radar and television receivers and transmitters and is of great value in many sciences.

AN AMPLIFIER WILL IMPROVE THE PERFORMANCE OF ANY OF THE RECEIVERS DESCRIBED IN THIS BOOK

A detector alone will not operate a loudspeaker. The power to operate the speaker in a broadcast receiver is secured by sending the signals from the detector into an amplifier. An amplifier called a radio-frequency amplifier strengthens the radio frequency currents before they reach the detector. The amplifier which strengthens the signals after they pass through the detector is an audio-frequency amplifier.

It is not easy for the beginner at radio to make a radio-frequency amplifier but, fortunately, it is not difficult to build simple audio-frequency amplifiers. The construction of two audio-frequency amplifiers is described in this chapter. Either one, added to any of the crystal detector receivers or to the one-tube receiver, will greatly increase the strength of the signals heard in the headphones and sometimes will operate a small speaker.

An amplifier which employs one tube is called a single-stage amplifier. An amplifier which feeds the amplified current from one tube into a second tube is a two-stage amplifier. Each tube and its circuit is a stage. Amplifiers of many stages are often used in electronics.

HOW TO BUILD A ONE-STAGE AUDIO AMPLIFIER

The parts required to build the one-tube amplifier are:

1 Wood base, 6 x 4¾ x ¾ inches
1 6BF6 receiving tube
1 Audio input transformer 3 to 1 ratio
1 100,000-ohm, ½-watt resistor
1 7-pin miniature tube socket
7 Connectors or binding posts, whichever you prefer
   Hook-up wire and solder
2 No. 5 round head brass screws ⅝-inch long
7 Screws for fastening the connectors or binding posts
2 Screws and spacers for fastening the socket
   Shellac and brush

The tools required are a screwdriver, cutting pliers, soldering iron, ruler, pencil, a hand drill if you use binding posts, and whatever woodworking tools may be necessary to cut out the base.

The first step is to make the base from a piece of smooth, DRY wood. Dry is emphasized because current will leak and weaken signals if a piece of damp or unseasoned wood is used. The base should measure about 6 x 4¾ x ¾ inches but it is not neces-

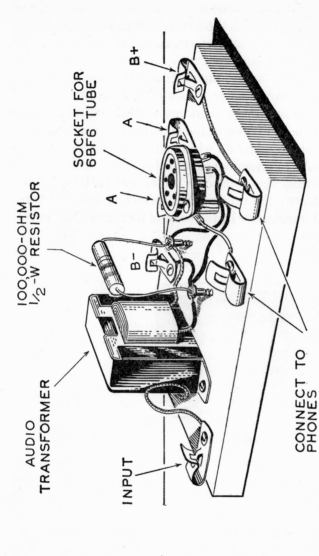

AUDIO
TRANSFORMER

100,000-OHM
$\frac{1}{2}$-W RESISTOR

SOCKET FOR
6BF6 TUBE

B+

A

A

B−

INPUT

CONNECT TO
PHONES

ONE-STAGE AUDIO AMPLIFIER

A homemade device which will greatly strengthen the signals of any of
the receivers described in the preceding chapters.

sary to make it exactly these dimensions. It can be ½ inch instead of ¾ inch thick. Wood thinner than this will usually warp more readily. Smooth the top and edges by sandpapering if necessary. Then give all surfaces two coats of shellac. The shellac will seal the wood.

When the shellac is dry, the parts can be mounted on the base. Fasten the two input terminals or posts at the left hand side of the base and the transformer to their right. The two input posts are used to connect the amplifier to a receiver.

It is advisable to solder all wiring and connections. Satisfactory connections to a vacuum tube socket are difficult to make without soldering. Use rosin core solder and push-back wire.

You can identify the primary and secondary terminal wires on a standard transformer by the color of their insulating cover-

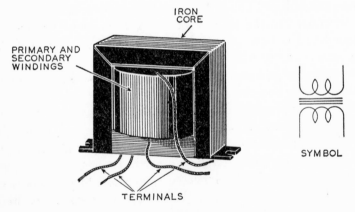

AUDIO TRANSFORMER

Three or four hundred types and sizes of transformers are listed in radio catalogs. The transformer used in building the one-stage amplifier is described as a "low-priced audio-interstage transformer for single plate to single grid, one to three ratio." If you ask for a transformer in the words above which are enclosed in quotation marks, a radio dealer will understand your requirements. If the transformer is not in stock, it can be ordered for you from a wholesaler. The price should not be more than two dollars. There are high-priced interstage transformers available but a high quality transformer is not required for this amplifier.

ing. The primary wires are blue and red; the secondary wires are green and black. The wires may be coated with wax or paraffin and the colors faint and difficult to read. In that case the colors can be made clearly visible by applying a warm (not hot) soldering iron on the insulation for an instant. Connect the blue primary wire to one of the input posts and the red primary wire to the other. Set two No. 5 round head brass screws ⅝-inch long into the wood base to the right of the transformer and 1½ inches apart. Solder the green secondary wire (this is also called the grid wire) to the head of one of the screws. Solder the black secondary wire to the head of the other screw.

Twist the end of one of the wire terminals on a 100,000 ohm, ½ watt resistor around one of the screws and solder it in place. Twist the end of the resistor's other terminal around the second screw and solder it. This will connect the resistor directly across the secondary of the transformer. The tube socket should be fastened to the base at the right of the resistor. Connect the brass screw (x) to which the green secondary or green wire is soldered to the grid terminal (No. 1) on the tube socket. Solder the connection between the wire and the socket.

The output terminals or posts on the amplifier are those to which the phones or loud speaker are connected when the amplifier is in operation. They are located at the right and front of the base. The battery posts are located along the rear edge of the base toward the right-hand end. Mark these posts from left to right B—, A, A and B+ as shown in several of the illustrations. Black pencil marks on the wood base alongside each terminal will suffice. One of the terminals marked A is connected to contact No. 3 on the socket. The other A terminal is connected to the No. 4 socket terminal. The negative terminal of the B battery is connected to the B— terminal on the amplifier. A wire connected to the B— terminal on the amplifier should also be connected to the No. 2 (cathode) socket terminal and to the brass screw (Z) to which the black secondary wire from the transformer is connected. A wire attached to one

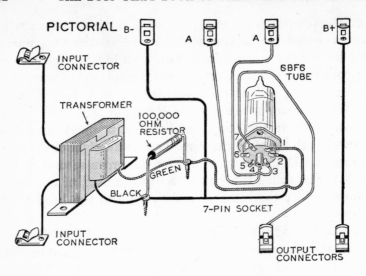

PICTORIAL

INPUT CONNECTOR

TRANSFORMER

100,000 OHM RESISTOR

GREEN

BLACK

INPUT CONNECTOR

B-

A

A

B+

6BF6 TUBE

7-PIN SOCKET

OUTPUT CONNECTORS

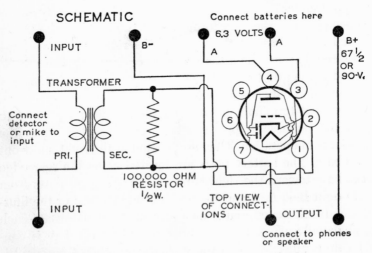

SCHEMATIC

Connect batteries here

6.3 VOLTS

INPUT

B-

A

A

B+
67 1/2
OR
90-V.

TRANSFORMER

Connect detector or mike to input

PRI.   SEC.

100,000 OHM RESISTOR 1/2 W.

TOP VIEW OF CONNECTIONS

INPUT

OUTPUT

Connect to phones or speaker

PICTORIAL AND SCHEMATIC CIRCUIT
DIAGRAMS OF THE ONE-STAGE AMPLIFIER

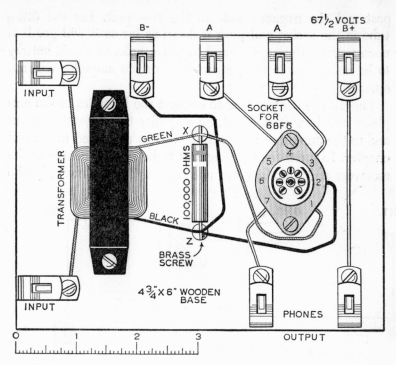

PLAN OF ONE-STAGE
TRANSFORMER-COUPLED AUDIO-AMPLIFIER

phone or output terminal should be connected to No. 7 (plate) terminal on the socket. The other phone terminal post is connected to the B+ terminal post.

If you consult both the pictorial and schematic diagrams you should not have difficulty in wiring the amplifier correctly. As in all radio work, use only rosin-core solder for soldering. A 67½-volt B battery and a 6-volt source of heater current are required to operate the amplifier. A 6-volt dry battery, a 6-volt storage battery, or a 6.3-volt AC supply from a filament transformer can be used to supply heater current. The two wires supplying heater current should be connected to binding post terminals A and A. Use a 6BF6 tube and a 67½- or 90-volt B battery. Connect the positive pole of the B battery to the B+

post and the negative pole to the B— post. Put the 6BF6 tube in the socket and push it down as far as it will go. It is necessary for the positive and negative poles of the B battery to be connected to the proper posts or the amplifier will not operate.

The diagrams show how to connect the batteries to the amplifier and how to connect the amplifier to a crystal receiver and to the one-tube regenerative receiver described in the last chapter. In order for the diagrams to be simple, details of the receivers and amplifier are not shown. They show only the

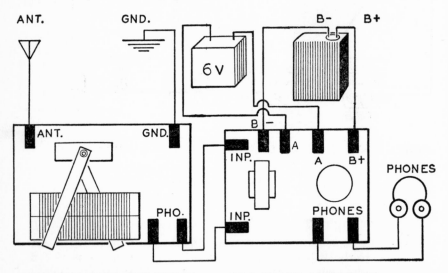

DOUBLE-SLIDER RECEIVER   ONE-STAGE AMPLIFIER

HOW TO CONNECT THE ONE-STAGE AMPLIFIER
TO A CRYSTAL RECEIVER

The diagram above shows how to connect the double-slider receiver to the one-stage amplifier. The PHONE posts on the receiver are connected to the INPUT posts on the amplifier and the phones are shifted to the OUTPUT posts on the amplifier. Any of the receivers with a crystal detector can be connected to the amplifier in the same manner. The batteries play no part in the operation of the crystal detector, their energy is utilized solely by the amplifier.

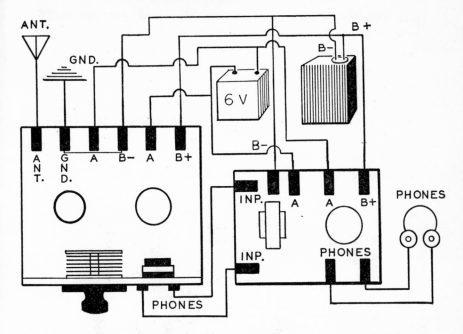

REGENERATIVE RECEIVER   ONE-STAGE AMPLIFIER

HOW TO CONNECT THE AMPLIFIER
TO THE ONE-TUBE REGENERATIVE RECEIVER

The PHONES posts on the receiver are connected to the INPUT posts on
the amplifier. A pair of phones or a small loudspeaker (4 to 5 inch) are
connected to the output posts of the amplifier. The receiver and amplifier
use the same B battery and the same source of A current. The switch
on the volume control on the receiver turns the heater current on and off
in the receiver only. It does not control the heater current in the amplifier
tube. When the apparatus is not in use a wire should be disconnected
from an A terminal post on both the receiver and the amplifier to prevent waste of current.

bases of the instruments and the terminal posts. Diagrams of
this type are the "block" diagrams used often in radio books.

The amplifier does not require any tuning or adjustment. It
is not provided with an "on-off" switch and in order to preserve
the batteries, they should always be disconnected when the
amplifier is not in use.

When strong signals come in through a receiver, the amplifier will increase their strength sufficiently so that a small loudspeaker of the permanent magnet type can be used in place of the headphones. The speaker (4 or 5-inch) must be one provided with a matching transformer. In this arrangement, the secondary of the matching transformer is connected to the voice coil in the speaker and the primary terminals of the transformer are connected to the output posts of the amplifier in place of the headphones. Speakers can be purchased equipped with a matching transformer already connected to the voice coil.

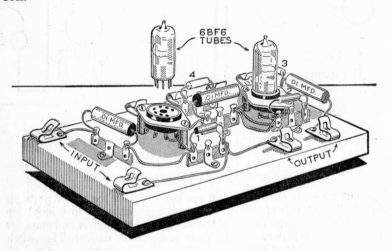

TWO-STAGE RESISTANCE-COUPLED AMPLIFIER

HOW TO BUILD A TWO-STAGE AMPLIFIER

Nowadays, the audio-frequency amplifiers built into broadcast receivers do not usually employ audio-frequency transformers. They use resistance coupling in place of transformer coupling. The amplifier described above is a resistance-coupled amplifier.

For the sake of simplicity and to make the two-stage amplifier easy for the radio beginner to build, the triode sections of two multi-unit tubes are used. This is simpler than using pentode (five element) tubes.

The following parts and materials are used in building the two-stage amplifier:

1 Wood base 8⅜ x 4¾ x ¾ inches
2 6BF6 radio tubes
2 7-pin miniature sockets
3 .01 Mfd, 400-volt paper capacitors
2 100,000-ohm, ½-watt resistors
5 2-terminal Bakelite terminal strips
5 Screws for mounting terminals
4 Screws and spacers for mounting sockets
8 Fahnestock connectors and mounting screws

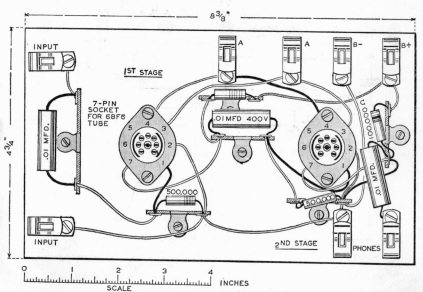

PLAN OF THE RESISTANCE-COUPLED AMPLIFIER

2 500,000-ohm, ½ watt resistors
8 Connectors or binding posts
4 Screws for fastening the sockets
8 Screws for fastening the connectors or binding posts
Hookup wire and solder
Shellac and brush

The tools required are a screwdriver, cutting pliers, soldering iron, ruler, pencil, a hand drill if you use binding posts and whatever woodworking tools may be necessary to make the base.

The base should be thoroughly dry and all of its surfaces given two coats of shellac varnish. The plan of the amplifier which is illustrated shows how the parts are arranged on the base.

Eight terminal posts are provided for connecting the amplifier to a receiver, batteries, phones, speaker, etc. The current

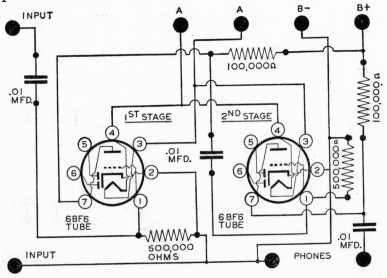

SCHEMATIC CIRCUIT DIAGRAM
OF THE TWO-STAGE RESISTANCE-COUPLED AMPLIFIER

This diagram and the plan will enable you to wire the amplifier.

B+ and B—). Place a 6BF6 tube in each socket and the amplifier is ready to operate.

Connect the output posts of a crystal detector receiver or
the one tube receiver to the input posts on the amplifier. Connect a pair of phones to the output posts on the amplifier. No
tuning or adjustment of the amplifier is necessary. If you have
wired it correctly, if the component parts are in good condition,
it will operate when supplied with proper current. Disconnect
the A battery when the amplifier is not in use.

AN INTERESTING EXPERIMENT WITH AN AMPLIFIER

If you build the one-tube amplifier you can use it to demonstrate how a vacuum tube is used to strengthen the feeble currents which carry telephone messages to distant points. Until
1915 the telephones of the Bell System consisted essentially of a
call bell, a transmitter, a receiver, an induction coil and a
battery. By means of switchboards located in central offices, a
telephone could be connected to any other telephone desired.
With this equipment it was impractical to talk over telephone
lines more than 1000 miles long. Then the special form of amplifier called a "repeater" was added to the telephone system,
making long distance telephony possible between any places
where wires can be stretched, no matter how far.

In order to demonstrate the action of your amplifier in
strengthening currents which produce speech and sounds, a
microphone is needed. A microphone is an apparatus for changing faint sounds into variations in an electric current. When
sounds strike a microphone, an electric current flowing through
the microphone is changed in strength in rhythm with the
vibrations of the sounds. There are many varieties of microphones. A telephone transmitter is a form of microphone called
a carbon microphone.

Microphones were invented originally to improve the operation of Bell's first telephones. The first Bell telephones which
were installed for commercial service were clumsy and ineffi-

cient instruments with little resemblance to the telephones of today. Messages were shouted into a curious affair which looked like a wooden potato masher. Then, in order to hear the faint answer, the "potato masher" was held to the ear. The original Bell telephones had no battery and no separate transmitter—the same device served both as transmitter and receiver.

The telephone could not have come into wide use without a practical transmitter. A transmitter made it possible to use a battery. A battery furnishes much stronger currents than those which were generated by Bell's "potato masher."

The telephone transmitter in use today was developed over the years from inventions made by Thomas A. Edison, Emil Berliner, Professor David E. Hughes, Francis Balke, Henry Hunnings and an expert of the Bell Company named White.

One of the most valuable bits of knowledge used in the design of telephone transmitters was discovered by Professor Hughes. He demonstrated that a loose contact between the electrodes of a transmitter produced better results than a firm strong contact. The simple apparatus which Hughes devised to show this principle was the first microphone. He placed a small iron nail across two other nails which were part of a circuit containing a battery and a telephone receiver. The electrical contact between the nails was a "loose contact." When sound waves struck the nails, they vibrated slightly and varied the amount of current flowing through a telephone receiver. Later, Hughes improved his microphone by using carbon rods in place of nails.

HOW TO MAKE A MICROPHONE

You can make a sensitive microphone by arranging two pieces of carbon rod and a piece of pencil lead on a cardboard box.

MATERIALS NEEDED FOR THIS EXPERIMENT

1 Shallow cardboard box about 8 x 10 inches
2 Carbon rods from flashlight cells

4 Pieces of pencil lead from 1¼ to 4 inches long
2 Feet fine wire (Nos. 30 to 36 B.F.)
2 Binding posts or Fahnestock spring clips
2 1.5-volt dry cells
1 Single-tube amplifier with A and B battery
1 Radio headset

As you may know, pencil lead is not lead, it is graphite—a form of carbon. You can obtain the carbon rods from two old flashlight cells. Cut the cells open with a hacksaw and remove the carbon electrode. This is a carbon rod, fitted with a brass cap and it is in the center of the cell. Do not remove the brass cap from the end of the rod. Rub the rods with a piece of fine sandpaper to remove any of the black powder which may adhere to its surface. Brighten the metal cap on each rod. Then solder a fine copper wire (Nos. 30 to 36 B.S.), about one foot long, to each brass cap. Fine wire is used because large wire interferes with the vibration of the carbon rods when they are moved by sound waves.

A cardboard box about 10 or 12 inches long and 8 or 9 inches wide is used as a sounding board. The box cover is discarded. Turn the box upside down and fasten the carbon rods to the bottom of the box with sealing wax. The rods should be near the center, parallel to one another and about one inch apart.

Use a sharp knife to split a wooden pencil so as to obtain the lead. Or, if you prefer, buy some 4-inch lead refills for an automatic pencil. Four pieces of lead are required—the shortest should be about 1¼ inches long, the longest piece should measure 4 inches and the other two respectively 2 and 3 inches long. Cut or file a narrow, shallow groove across each carbon rod midway between the ends. It is easy to make the grooves with the edges of a 3-cornered file. Do not make them any deeper than a deep scratch. Cut them only deep enough to prevent the pencil lead from rolling off the carbons when it is laid in the grooves.

Mount two binding posts or Fahnestock spring clips on the

end of the box and connect the ends of the wires attached to the carbon rods to them.

The microphone is now ready to test. Connect two or three 1.5-volt dry cells in series and then connect them and a radio headset to the microphone so that any current which flows

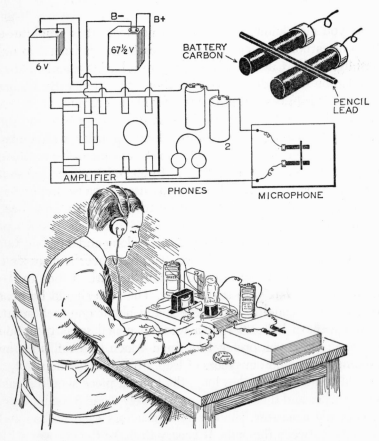

AN EXPERIMENT WHICH WILL DEMONSTRATE
THE POWER OF YOUR AMPLIFIER

The circuit diagram at the top shows how to connect the microphone to the amplifier. Dry cell No. 1 supplies current to the filament of the amplifier tube. Dry cell No. 2 supplies current to the microphone circuit.

through the headphones from the battery must also pass through the microphone. Place one of the pieces of pencil lead across the carbon rods. Place it in the grooves so that it will not roll off. If all connections have been made properly any sounds made near the microphone will produce sounds in the telephone receivers. Any slight vibration made by touching the table upon which the microphone is resting or by touching the box itself will also produce sounds in the receivers. The ticking of a watch lying on or near the box and the noises which its wheels make, ordinarily inaudible to human ears, can also be heard in the receivers. One piece of pencil lead may produce better results than the others, try all four.

To see the effect of the one-tube amplifier* in increasing the current flowing in the telephone receivers and consequently the sounds produced thereby, connect the microphone and a 1.5-volt dry cell to the input terminals of the amplifier. Connect a 6-volt A battery and a 67½-volt B battery to the proper terminals and the telephone headset to the output terminals. Words spoken close to the microphone will be reproduced in the telephone receivers, distinctly enough to be understood but not quite as clearly as would be the case if the microphone were a modern telephone transmitter. The operation of the microphone and amplifier in picking up and reproducing speech can best be appreciated when the wires leading from the output terminals of the amplifier to the radio headset are long enough so that the microphone can be located in one room and the headset in an adjoining room.

---

* The carbon microphone circuit, as described here, will not work with the two-stage, resistance coupled amplifier.

CHAPTER ELEVEN

THE ANTENNA AND GROUND FOR YOUR HOMEMADE RADIO RECEIVER— HOW TO SOLDER

One of the necessary parts of every radio receiver is the antenna. It intercepts the incoming waves. The waves produce very small alternating currents in the antenna. The antenna current is sent through the detector. The simplest antenna is a length of wire. It may be either vertical or horizontal. A long wire is more efficient than a short one for receiving long waves (low frequencies). A short wire is most suitable for intercepting short waves (high frequencies).

The amount of energy represented by the electric currents created in a receiving antenna is very small, probably only a few billionths of a watt. Therefore it is important to arrange the antenna so that it will collect and conserve as much energy as possible. More energy picked up by the antenna and fed to the receiver results in louder signals from the headphones or speaker.

The best antenna for any of the receivers described in this book is a wire 50-75 feet long, properly insulated, clear of surrounding objects and as high as possible. A height of 30-50 feet above ground is desirable. The most desirable supports for an antenna are two sturdy poles. Such supports are not always available and sometimes a building or a tree must be used as a support. When a tree supports one end, remember

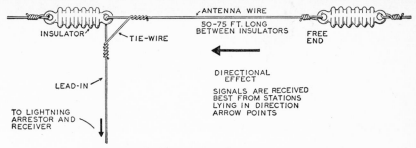

INSULATOR
TIE-WIRE
ANTENNA WIRE
50-75 FT. LONG
BETWEEN INSULATORS
FREE END
DIRECTIONAL EFFECT
SIGNALS ARE RECEIVED BEST FROM STATIONS LYING IN DIRECTION ARROW POINTS
LEAD-IN
TO LIGHTNING ARRESTOR AND RECEIVER

THE ANTENNA FOR YOUR RECEIVER

The best antenna for your homemade receiver is a single horizontal hard drawn No. 14 B.S. copper wire 50 to 75 feet long and insulated from its supports at both ends.

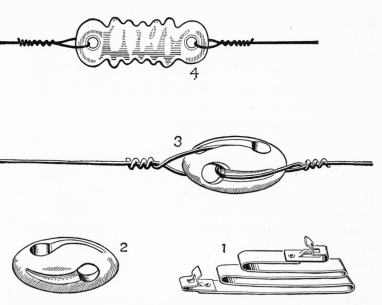

ANTENNA INSULATORS

1. An insulated lead-in window strip makes it easy to lead in the antenna over a window sill and under the sash without interfering with the opening or closing of the window. 2, 3. Porcelain strain insulator commonly used to insulate the guy wires which brace an antenna support but can also be used as antenna insulators. 4. Corrugated glass antenna insulator.

that the antenna should hang slack so that if the tree sways in the wind it will not strain or break the wire.

When possible, locate the antenna where it will not be close to chimneys, tin roofs, gutters, drain pipes, walls, telephone wires, power wires and tree branches. Use No. 14 B. S. hard drawn bare copper wire or the stranded copper antenna wire obtainable at radio shops. The antenna and the wire which leads from the antenna to the receiver (called the lead-in wire) should be a continuous piece (no splices). Use at least one 3-inch glass antenna insulator at each end of the antenna.

All antennas, except a single vertical wire, have a directional effect. This means that a horizontal wire whose length is greater than its height above ground will receive signals slightly better in one direction than in others. It will receive best in the direction opposite to that toward which the free end points. The free end is the end opposite that to which the lead-in is attached.

If you have a choice and can arrange your antenna to point in any desired direction, erect it so that its directional effect will be an advantage in bringing in signals from the station you prefer to hear.

Antennas on Apartment Houses. In cities, a radio antenna often encounters problems which are not met with in the suburbs. These are such things as telephone wires running over roofs, nearby TV and radio antennas, steel frame buildings and man-made static. Man-made static is the noise produced in radio receivers by elevators, refrigerators, vacuum cleaners and other electrical devices. When possible, a radio antenna on the roof of an apartment house should be supported by two wooden poles at least ten feet above the roof. It should be at right angles to neighboring wires or antennas. The only antenna it may be practicable to install on some premises may be a vertical wire suspended from the edge of the roof and leading down to a lower window.

The Lead-in. The lead-in from a single wire antenna should be the same sort of wire as the antenna. It should not approach the side of the building closer than six inches except at the point where it enters. The best method to bring the lead-in wire into a house and avoid leakage of energy is to pass it through a porcelain tube in the wall or window frame. As an alternative, an antenna lead-in strip may be used. This device is a strip of copper insulated with waterproof lacquered webbing which is thin enough so that it may be laid on the window sill and the window can be pulled down on it and closed.

DOES AN ANTENNA ATTRACT LIGHTNING?

Since the ordinary amateur antenna is usually comparatively close to the ground, it does not attract lightning. There is no more chance that lightning will strike a building if it has the common form of low, arrester-protected receiving antenna than there would be if it had none.

However, if lightning strikes in the neighborhood, an antenna may pick up a considerable electrical charge and this can do damage unless a lightning arrester is provided. The National Board of Fire Insurance Underwriters requires that any antenna erected on insured property be protected by a suitable lightning arrester. An antenna without a lightning arrester is a violation of the Fire Insurance Code which can render an insurance policy worthless.

A lightning arrester for the antenna of a radio receiver is an inexpensive device placed on the outside wall of a building at the point where the lead-in enters. The arrester usually is a small spark-gap sealed in a vacuum so that the gap can be jumped by a low voltage charge. One side of the arrester is connected to the lead-in, the other to the ground outside the building. A ground rod, for driving into the earth and connecting to the lightning arrester, is obtainable at a radio shop at small cost. It is a copper-plated steel rod four to six feet long, fitted with a connecting clamp.

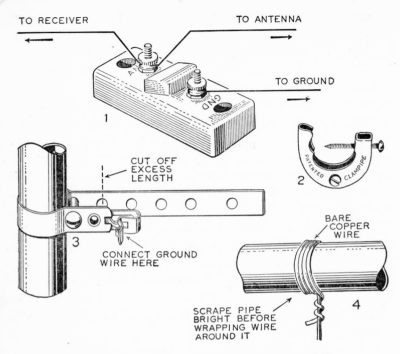

TO RECEIVER

TO ANTENNA

TO GROUND

1

CUT OFF
EXCESS
LENGTH

2

3

CONNECT GROUND
WIRE HERE

BARE
COPPER
WIRE

4

SCRAPE PIPE
BRIGHT BEFORE
WRAPPING WIRE
AROUND IT

LIGHTNING ARRESTOR AND GROUND CONNECTIONS

1. Attach the lightning arrestor to an outside wall, preferably near a window. Connect the terminal marked ANT to the antenna and to the lead-in which conducts the antenna into the building. Connect the terminal marked GND to a ground outside the house. 2, 3. Ground clamps for connecting ground wires to water pipes. A wire can be connected to a water pipe by wrapping several turns around the pipe.

INDOOR ANTENNAS

When an antenna cannot be erected outdoors, an indoor antenna may produce satisfactory signals in a homemade receiver. The wire can be a small one (No. 25 B. S. gauge) which is easily concealed behind a picture molding or under rugs or carpets. The wire should be as long as possible. An indoor antenna is not as efficient as an outdoor antenna and may not be at all useful if located in a steel frame building. If wire covered with insulation is used, it is not necessary to support the wire with insulators.

THE GROUND

A good connection to the ground as well as an antenna are necessary to secure satisfactory signals from the homemade receivers. In town and cities a good ground connection can be made to a water pipe. Second choice is a connection made to steam or hot water heating pipes. No matter which type of pipe is used, the pipe should be scraped, sandpapered or filed bright and clean at the point where the connection is to be made. Use a ground clamp to connect the wire to the pipe. On farms or in the country where no water or steam pipes are available a ground connection can be secured by driving two pieces of galvanized pipe or ground rods six feet long into the earth five or six feet apart and connecting the ground wire to the top of both pipes or rods. This type of ground will not prove satisfactory in dry or sandy soil. Select a spot where the earth is damp, if such is available.

HOW TO SOLDER

Soldering metals together forms a good electrical connection between them. An electric current will flow more easily through the splice between two pieces of wire twisted together if the splice is soldered. Therefore a soldering iron is an important tool to a radio mechanic—whether he be a boy building an amplifier or a professional at work on a complicated television receiver. He uses a soldering iron to join wires together and to connect wires to terminals.

Anyone can learn to solder—it is not difficult. The ability to make a good soldered joint is useful for many purposes other than building or repairing radio apparatus. You can use this skill to mend electrical equipment, toys, kitchen utensils, etc.

A soldering iron, solder and a flux are used to solder radio apparatus.

Solder is an alloy which has the appearance of lead. An alloy is a mixture of metals. Common solder is a mixture of lead and tin. It can be purchased at hardware stores. Dime stores also sell solder. It is available in the form of bars, strips and wire. Wire solder is most convenient for radio and small electrical work. It may be either cored or solid. Cored solder is a small tube filled with some form of flux.

Fluxes are chemicals used in soldering to clean the metal so that the molten solder will stick to it. It is very difficult to solder without a flux. The common fluxes are rosin, sal ammoniac and certain acid compounds which may be either in fluid or paste form.

Sal ammoniac, soldering paste and liquid soldering acid are useful for "tinning" a soldering iron (tinning will be explained later) and for soldering large work which can be washed afterward so that all traces of the flux are removed. These fluxes will corrode small wires and also will cause short circuits in radio and electrical work. Rosin is the only flux to use in soldering radio apparatus. Wire solder with a rosin core is most convenient and satisfactory for radio work.

Before a metal can be soldered it must be hot enough to melt solder. In radio work the heat is supplied by:

Soldering Irons. A small electric iron (75- or 100-watt size) is the most desirable but of course is useless unless electric power is available. An old-fashioned iron which is heated in the flame of a gas stove, blowtorch, Bunsen burner or a charcoal fire can be used in place of an electric iron and costs less.

The temperature of a fire-heated iron must be watched closely. If you use this type of iron, remove it from the fire from time to time and test its temperature by rubbing the tip of the iron against a piece of solder. The tip must be clean and well-tinned for this test. If the solder melts freely, the iron is hot enough. The iron should not be allowed to become red hot or remain in the fire longer than necessary. If overheated, a coating of copper oxide will form on the surface and the tinning on

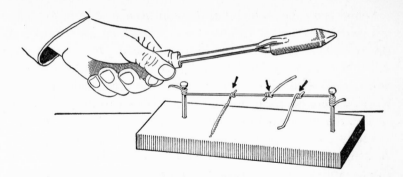

SOLDERING PRACTICE

If you are a novice at soldering, practice on scraps of wire before soldering connections on a receiver or amplifier. The iron in the sketch is the fire-heated type.

the tip will be destroyed. When an iron has been overheated, mechanics call it a burned iron and it must be retinned before it can be used.

To Tin an Iron the tip should be filed smooth and bright with a coarse file. Then heat it until it is hot enough to melt solder. Before the tip has a chance to cool it is brightened again by a few light strokes of a file and rubbed with ACID core solder until the surface of the tip is well coated with solder.

An electric iron will become overheated and the tinning will be burned off the tip if the iron remains connected to the power supply for a long time without being used. When this occurs the tip must be filed and retinned in the same manner as a fire-heated iron.

Practice. If you have never done any soldering it is advisable to practice on a few pieces of wire before you try to solder connections on radio apparatus. Cut some scrap copper wire into pieces about four inches long to experiment with. Remove the insulation from the ends for a distance of about one-half inch and brighten the exposed copper. Drive two common nails (about three inches apart) into a block of wood. Twist the ends two of the wires together so as to form a splice. Stretch the wires between the two nails so that the splice is in the middle and twist the free ends of the wires around the nails. Hold one of the flat faces on the tip of a hot soldering iron against the side of the splice. When the iron has heated the splice for two or three seconds, push the end of a piece of rosin core solder against the iron where it touches the wire. If the iron is held correctly you will be able to touch the splice and the iron at the same time with the solder and the solder will melt and flow into the splice. If the solder melts but is "mushy," the iron is not hot enough or is not well tinned. Dirt on the tip will prevent

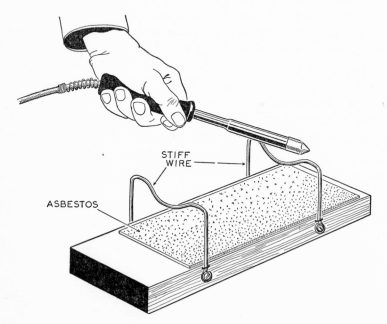

STIFF WIRE

ASBESTOS

SOLDERING IRON REST

When soldering radio apparatus, it is necessary to lay down the soldering iron from time to time. It should rest where it will not be cooled by contact and where it will not scorch or burn anything. Make a soldering iron rest out of a block of wood, a piece of asbestos paper and the wire from a wire coat hanger as illustrated above.

the iron from heating the solder. An experienced solderer occasionally wipes the hot tip of his iron against a rag to clean it. The molten solder should be hot enough to flow like water.

A second or so after the solder flows into the splice, remove the iron and let the splice cool undisturbed. When cold, the surface of the solder on the splice should be bright and shining. If the solder has a dull surface, it is a "cold" splice, and unsatisfactory. The iron was not hot enough or the splice was disturbed while cooling and should be soldered over again. There is no advantage in using so much solder that it forms a lump on the splice.

When you have soldered the splice between one pair of wires, unwind them from the nails and continue your practice with other pairs until you can make a neat job of soldering a splice. Then you are qualified to solder the connections on radio apparatus.

Remember that ACID core solder may be used for tinning an iron but it is never used for soldering radio or electrical apparatus. Be careful where you lay a hot soldering iron. It is worth while to take the time to make a stand or rest for the iron as shown in one of the illustrations. A piece of wood, two screws and a wire coat hanger are the only materials required.

CHAPTER TWELVE

LEARNING TO SEND AND RECEIVE
RADIO TELEGRAPH SIGNALS

From time to time while "listening in" with the one-tube regenerative receiver, you may hear radiotelegraph signals. These will convey no meaning to you unless you know the Continental Code used in radiotelegraphy. Learning to receive telegraph signals is mostly a matter of practice and is not difficult.

You will enjoy radio more if you can "read" radiotelegraph signals. You can listen to amateurs, ships and shore stations and understand their messages. You can also obtain a government license to operate a transmitter of your own. The first step is to memorize the alphabet so that the sound of each character can be instantly called to mind. From the beginning always think of the SOUNDS of the characters and not of the dots and dashes by which they are represented on paper. A dot should be the sound DIT and a dash the sound DAH in your mind. Think and speak of the letter A as dit dah and not as dot dash; the letter B as dah dit dit dit, etc.

Commercial radio operators and most amateurs send too fast for a beginner to read at first. But if you concentrate on the dit and dah sounds and do not think of dots and dashes you will

216

THE CONTINENTAL CODE

A B C D E F

G H I J K

L M N O P

Q R S T U

V W X Y

Z

1 2 3

4 5 6 7

8 9 0

Call Invitation to Transmit

Period Interrogation Break

Wait End of message End of transmission

Received Go ahead Comma

THE CONTINENTAL CODE

, able to recognize letters now and then. The first letters you are able to identify will probably be the dot letters:

E dit   I dit dit   S dit dit dit   H dit dit dit dit

and the letters

M dah dah   O dah dah dah   R dit dah dit   K dah dit dah
A dit dah   N dah dit and T dah

Phonograph code records provide the best way to learn to "read" telegraph signals. The complete course of lessons for beginners consists of five double-faced unbreakable Vinylite records. The lessons begin with the sounds of telegraph signals at the rate of two words a minute. Any one can copy at that rate after a few minutes practice. Two words a minute is the equivalent of a letter every 6 seconds. The speed is gradually increased as the lessons progress. The last record produces the signal sounds at the rate of 15 words a minute.

A set of five records costs about ten dollars. One way to solve the problem of their purchase price is to form a code club. If five or six beginners "chip in" the cost to each member will be only about two dollars.

A CODE-PRACTICE SET

The ability of a radio telegraph operator to send well-formed code characters with a key is just as important as is his ability to recognize and record them accurately. You can easily build a code-practice set. With it, you can learn to send. It will also help you to memorize the code characters and to recognize their sound. Buy a standard telegraph key, a high-frequency buzzer, two binding posts and one or two No. 6 dry cells. Connect them in series so that pressing the key will operate the buzzer. A high-frequency buzzer produces a high-pitched sound similar to the sound of a radiotelegraph signal. If you adjust the contact screw and the tension screw on the buzzer properly, you will obtain a good imitation of radio signals.

Mount the key, buzzer and binding posts on a piece of ¼-inch plywood or ⅛-inch Masonite as shown in the illustration. One terminal of the key is the frame, the other is the lower (stationary) contact. Drill two holes in the wooden or Masonite base to line up with the holes in the base of the buzzer, so that the wires which connect the key, buzzer and binding posts can be run on the under side of the base. One wire should connect one of the binding posts to the stationary contact on the key. A second wire should connect the second binding post to one of the terminals of the buzzer. The other buzzer terminal should be connected to the key frame.

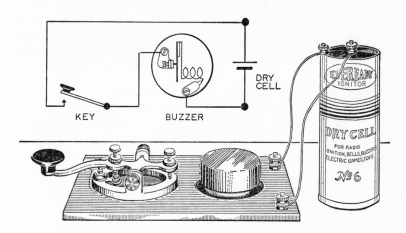

KEY AND BUZZER FOR CODE PRACTICE

How to Adjust the Key. You cannot learn to telegraph well with a key which is improperly adjusted. The contact on the underside of the lever should be directly over the stationary contact on the key base. If it is not, loosen the lock nuts on the trunnion screws and adjust the screws so as to bring the hammer to the proper position. Tighten the lock nuts on the trunnion screws. The key lever should work freely up and down without any side play.

The space between the contact on the underside of the lever and the stationary contact on the key frame should be about 0.008 inch when the key lever is up. Use three thicknesses of bond typewriter paper as a gauge. The thickness of three sheets of this paper is about 0.0008 inch. If the space between the contacts is too small or too large, loosen the lock nut on the adjusting screw and turn the screw until the space between the contacts is 0.008. Tighten the lock nut.

Loosen the lock nut on the tension screw and turn the screw to adjust the spring tension. The tension should permit the key lever to be pushed down easily with the finger tips, yet be great enough to push the lever up sharply when the pressure is released. If the tension is not great enough, your sending will be characterized by dots which are too long and by irregular spacing between characters. Too much tension results in short dashes, dot skipping and long spacing between characters.

How to Hold the Key.   The position of the fingers on the key is important. If you start your code practice by holding the key properly, it will not be necessary to correct any bad habit later.

The key should be back from the edge of the table far enough so that when your fingers rest on the key knob your elbow can rest on the table. Rest the tips of the first and second fingers lightly but firmly on top of the key knob. Hold the thumb lightly against the edge of the key knob. The first joints of the first and second fingers should be held nearly vertical and not horizontal. Curve the third and fourth fingers under the palm of the hand. The fingers should be relaxed and without tension or rigidity.

Check your position and if necessary correct it so that:

1. Your forearm is in line with the key lever.
2. Your elbow and not your forearm rests on the table.
3. Your wrist is about 1½ inches above the table and not resting on it.
4. Your fingers are curved and flexible, not straight or stiff.

How to Operate the Key. When your hand and arm are in the correct position, press down the key knob with a straight downward motion of the forearm. In doing this, let the wrist bend downward slightly as if it were a hinge between your elbow and fingertips. Remember that:

A good operator uses his forearm and not his wrist and finger muscles. The key knob moves up and down because his forearm moves up and down. The hand and fingers are merely the medium through which the movements of the forearm are transmitted to the key. He avoids stiffness and rigidity in the fingers and wrist. Stiffness makes ragged signals, brings fatigue quickly and results in a "glass arm" (telegraph slang).

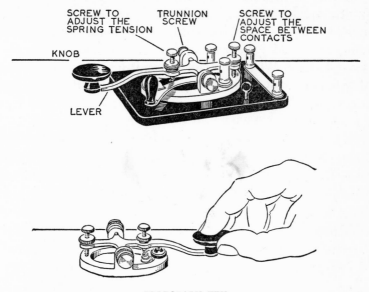

TELEGRAPH KEY

A telegraph key similar to that shown in the upper sketch is available from dealers in "ham" radio supplies. The drawing at the bottom shows a method of holding the key knob used by many professional telegraph operators. The forefinger rests on top of the key knob. The thumb and second finger grasp the edges of the knob and help the spring to raise the knob. The thumb and both fingers are used to press the knob down.

When the key contacts have been closed by a downward motion of the forearm, release the pressure on the knob and allow the spring to return it to the "up" position. Keep the thumb and fingers in light contact with the key knob. Do not raise them off the knob to allow the spring to return the key lever to the "up" position. Do not "tap" on the knob. A telegraph operator's thumb and fingers never leave the key knob until he has finished sending his message.

Transmitting Exercises. Place your code practice set on a table far enough back from the front edge so that you can take the correct sending position. Grasp the key and start making dots by pressing down the knob and releasing it immediately so that the buzzer makes a "dit" sound each time the key is pressed. Make dots at the rate of about 100 per minute. Do not make anything but dots. Try constantly to make the dots equal. If your arm and fingers become tired, rest for a short time, then transmit again. When you can transmit 30 dots in one group smoothly in about 10 seconds, you are ready to begin the next exercise.

Transmit the character V. It sounds like dit dit dit dah when made correctly. Hold the key down for the dah 3 times as long as you do to make a dit. Make the same time interval between the dits and between the third dit and the dah. Send smoothly. If you are trying to transmit faster than you should your sending will be rough. Send the V's at the rate of about 35 per minute. When you can send 20 consecutive V's smoothly at the rate of 35 per minute, you are ready to practice any letter in the code.

Learning to telegraph is like learning to play a musical instrument—practice helps more than anything else. Memorizing the code and learning to make the sounds of the characters are not the ultimate goal. Accuracy and speed are desirable. If you can get the assistance of an experienced operator, perhaps some one who already has an amateur radio operator's license and who will coach and criticize your sending, you will be in luck and progress more rapidly. Don't think that speed is important at first. Accuracy is more important. Speed will come with practice.

The best substitute for the assistance of an experienced operator is for two beginners to practice together—to take turns sending to each other with the code practice set.

Write down—"copy" it is called—the signals sent you, in the form of letters, numerals, and punctuation marks. Do not copy them as dots and dashes, for example, do not write a dot and dash for the letter A, write the letter A. If you do not recognize a character, leave a blank space. Do not think about an unrecognized character too long or you will miss the next signal. When you can send and receive 65 letters, numerals and punctuation marks per minute and copy them accurately, whether they make sense or not, you can pass a government code test. If you can pass the test and answer a few questions, you can obtain a "ham" operator's license.

REFERENCE BOOKS

Marconi: Pioneer of Radio by Douglas Coe, Messner

Father of Radio by Lee De Forest, Wilcox & Follett

Marconi, The Man and His Wireless by Orrin E. Dunlap, Jr.,
Macmillan

Radio's 100 Men of Science by Orrin E. Dunlap, Jr., Macmillan

Fessenden, Builder of Tomorrow by Helen M. Fessenden,
Coward-McCann

The Pageant of Electricity by Alfred P. Morgan, Appleton-
Century-Crofts

INDEX